Building Spelling Skills

Book 5

The World of Words

Written and designed by Garry J. Moes
Editors: Michael J. McHugh
Dr. Paul D. Lindstrom

A PUBLICATION OF
Christian Liberty Press

TABLE OF CONTENTS

PREFACE

Dear Teacher or Parent:

Book 5 of the *Building Spelling Skills* series is more than a spelling book. It is a mini-encyclopedia of spelling. One of the key purposes of studying the spelling of words, of course, is to prepare the student for the practical and accurate use of language in all the areas of knowledge. This book is designed to give the 5th-grade level student a wide-ranging journey through The World of Words. The book is, in a sense, inter-disciplinary. It not only gives the student practice in spelling words from a broad spectrum of subjects, but leads him or her into brief studies of the subjects themselves. In a literal recognition of the book's theme, the first six units help students learn to spell the names of the major countries and cities of the world, an increasingly important need as a global society grows in our time. The next two lessons guide youngsters on a journey across The United States of America to learn the names of the states and their capitals. Then comes a trek into the universe, and, finally, the book offers studies of words and terms used in a wide variety of favorite subjects.

In exploring the subjects of creation and human society, the student is guided also into God's Word. These explorations of the Word of God are intended to help the student realize the command of 2 Corinthians 10:5 to bring "into captivity every thought to the obedience of Christ." Instructors should help students see that the Scriptures indeed speak to every area of life and thought. In writing the Bible verses, students get additional practice in spelling words not on their weekly word lists.

Exercises are provided which will require, in many cases, consultations with dictionaries or other reference books. In some cases, elementary word definitions are supplied in the lesson; in other cases, students will be required to use a standard dictionary. Units involving geographical subjects may require reference to an atlas. If a comprehensive one is not available, students may use the limited world atlas provided at the back of the book.

As in other books in this series students are given numerous opportunities to write and rewrite each list word. Extensive practice, in the form of repetitive writing of the selected words, is a major tool in learning to spell English words. Most units also require the student to alphabetize their list words. While some students may find this exercise tedious, writing words in alphabetically order forces them to carefully examine the sequence of letters in each word, a useful aid in memorizing word spellings.

Lesson 3 in each unit beginning with Unit 7 includes an opportunity for a pre-test. The final lesson in each unit involves review and a final unit test. Test pages are provided beginning on page 114 which students should use to write their words.

Various word games and puzzles are included in some units. These are intended to guide the student into carefully recognizing the arrangement of letters and/or syllables in selected list words, an exercise which is important in light of the many irregularities in spelling the words of the English language.

Instructors are encouraged to keep reading and spelling in close fellowship with each other during the teaching process. It is also helpful to keep in mind that there are no shortcuts on the road to developing good spellers. Good spellers are developed by hard work and persistence on the part of both teacher and student.

ALPHABET

Aa Bb Cc Dd Ee Ff Gg Hh Ii Jj Kk Ll Mm

Nn Oo Pp Qq Rr Ss Tt Uu Vv Ww Xx Yy Zz

CURSIVE ALPHABET

Aa Bb Cc Dd Ee
Ff Gg Hh Ii Jj
Kk Ll Mm Nn
Oo Pp Qq Rr Ss
Tt Uu Vv Ww
Xx Yy Zz

LEARNING HOW TO SPELL WORDS

1. Look at the word. Study every letter.

2. Say the word to yourself.

3. Say it again aloud, and then spell it.

4. Copy the word on paper, naming the letters as you write.

5. Close your spelling book, and test yourself.
   Write the word.
   Do not worry if you do not get it right the first time.

6. Open your spelling book again. Check the word.

7. Study the word one more time, and test yourself
   by writing the word again.

* * * * *

As with all of your school work, always remember to ask God to help you learn and understand what you are doing. Thank Him for His help with every lesson.

U*NIT* 1

COUNTRIES OF THE WESTERN HEMISPHERE

United States	Ecuador
Canada	Bolivia
Mexico	Uruguay
Panama	Paraguay
Nicaragua	Venezuela
Guatemala	Argentina
El Salvador	Colombia
Honduras	Peru
Costa Rica	Brazil
Chile	Cuba

LESSON 1

Study these list words, using the study plan on page 7.

LESSON 2

Below are the names given to citizens of each of the countries on your word list. These words are also used as adjectives to describe things related to these countries. Learn the spelling of these adjective forms and write them.

American	_____	**Ecuadorian**	_____
Canadian	_____	**Bolivian**	_____
Mexican	_____	**Uruguayan**	_____
Panamanian	_____	**Paraguayan**	_____
Nicaraguan	_____	**Venezuelan**	_____
Guatemalan	_____	**Argentinian**	_____
Salvadoran	_____	**Colombian**	_____
Honduran	_____	**Peruvian**	_____
Costa Rican	_____	**Brazilian**	_____
Chilean	_____	**Cuban**	_____

LESSON 3

Using an encyclopedia, atlas, or the map on page 126, if necessary, identify the Western Hemisphere countries indicated below with list words.

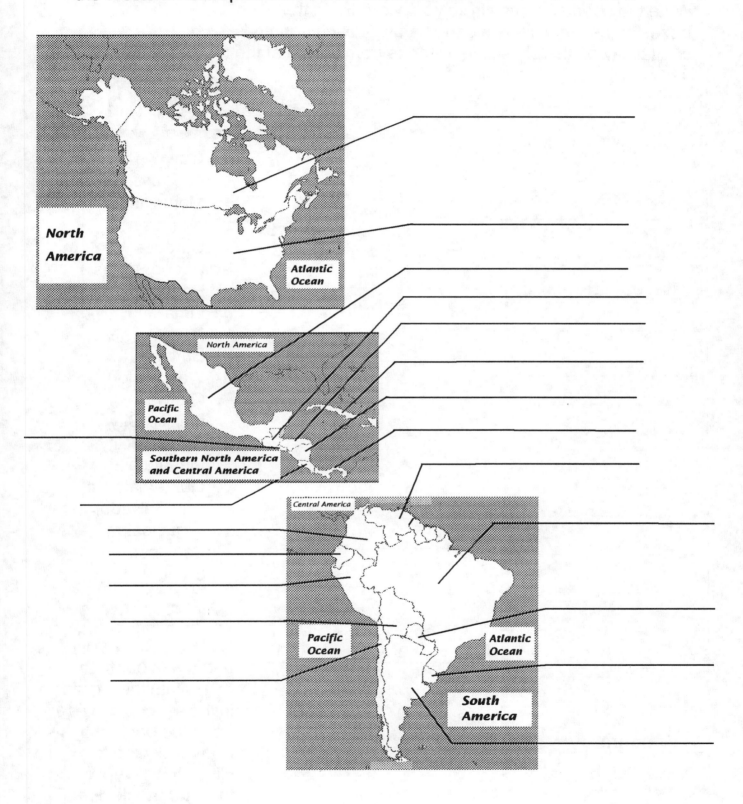

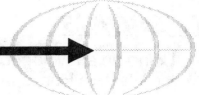

Write the country names from your word list in the boxes at the left. Then write the name of each country's capital city on the blank line. Choose from the list at the right.

Capitals

Quito
La Paz & Sucre
Montevideo
Asuncion
Caracas
Buenos Aires
Bogota
Lima
Brasilia
Havana
Washington
Ottawa
Mexico City
Panama City
Managua
Guatemala City
San Salvador
Tegucigalpa
San Jose
Santiago

LESSON 5

Review your word list and take your final test. Write the words in the spaces provided at the back of this book. Ask God for His help with your test and thank Him.

UNIT 2

COUNTRIES OF WESTERN EUROPE

France   Iceland
Ireland   Finland
England   Norway
Scotland   Sweden
The Netherlands Denmark
Germany   Northern Ireland
Portugal   Luxembourg
Belgium   Switzerland
Spain   Austria
Italy   Wales

LESSON 1

Study these list words, using the study plan on page 7.

LESSON 2

Below are adjectives used to describe things related to each of the countries on your word list. In most cases, these words are also the names of the natives and languages of these countries. Learn to spell the words and write them.

French _____   Icelandic* _____

Irish _____   Finnish _____

English _____   Norwegian _____

Scottish* _____   Swedish _____

Dutch _____   Danish _____

German _____   Luxembourgian* _____

Portuguese _____   Swiss _____

Belgian _____   Austrian _____

Spanish _____   Welsh* _____

Italian _____

*Scots and Scotch also describe the people and things of Scotland. Natives of Iceland are called Icelanders. Natives of Luxembourg are called Luxembourgers. The words Welsh and Welch can both be used with reference to Wales.

LESSON 3

1. Using an encyclopedia, atlas, or the map on 127, if necessary, identify the Western European countries indicated below with list words.

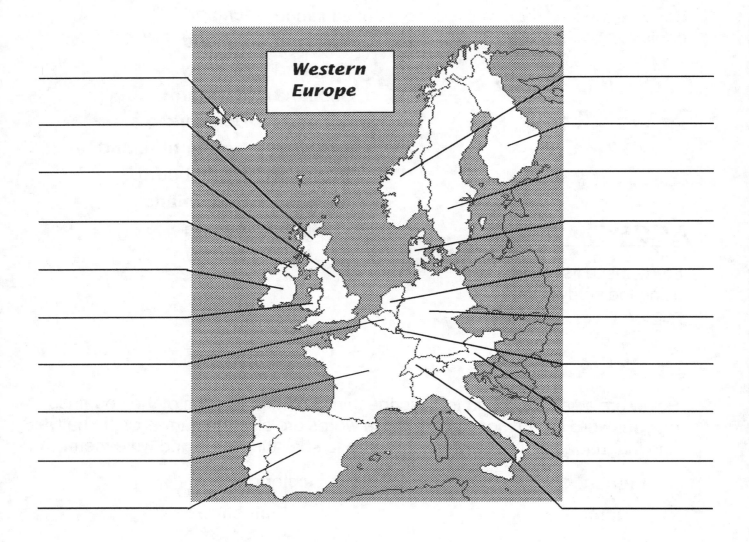

2. Write the country names from your word list in alphabetical order.

_____ _____ _____ _____

_____ _____ _____ _____

_____ _____ _____ _____

_____ _____ _____ _____

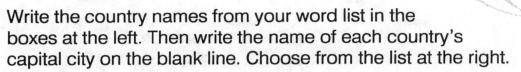

Write the country names from your word list in the boxes at the left. Then write the name of each country's capital city on the blank line. Choose from the list at the right.

Capitals

Reykjavik
Helsinki
Oslo
Stockholm
Copenhagen
Belfast
Luxembourg
Bern
Vienna
Cardiff (principal city)
Paris
Dublin
London
Edinburgh
Amsterdam/The Hague
Berlin
Lisbon
Brussels
Madrid
Rome

LESSON 5

Review your word list and take your final test. Write the words in the spaces provided at the back of this book. Ask God for His help with your test and thank Him.

U*NIT* 3

COUNTRIES OF EASTERN EUROPE

LESSON 1

Study these list words, using the study plan on page 7.

LESSON 2

Russia	Greece
Poland	Croatia
Hungary	Slovenia
Romania*	Yugoslavia**
Czech Republic	Bosnia-Hercegovina
Lithuania	Macedonia
Bulgaria	Belorussia***
Slovakia	Georgia
Albania	Ukraine
Latvia	Estonia

* Alternate spelling: Rumania
** Includes Serbia and Montenegro
*** Alternate spellings: Byelorussia,
Belarus or Byelarus

Below are adjectives used to describe things related to each of the countries on your word list. In most cases, these words are also the names of the natives and languages of these countries. Learn to spell the words and write them.

Russian	_____	**Greek**	_____
Polish	_____	**Croatian**	_____
Hungarian	_____	**Slovenian**	_____
Romanian	_____	**Yugoslavian**	_____
Czech	_____	**Bosnian**	_____
Lithuanian	_____	**Macedonian**	_____
Bulgarian	_____	**Belorussian**	_____
Slovakian	_____	**Georgian**	_____
Albanian	_____	**Ukrainian**	_____
Latvian	_____	**Estonian**	_____

LESSON 3

1. Using an encyclopedia, atlas, or the map on page 128, if necessary, identify the Eastern European countries indicated below with list words.

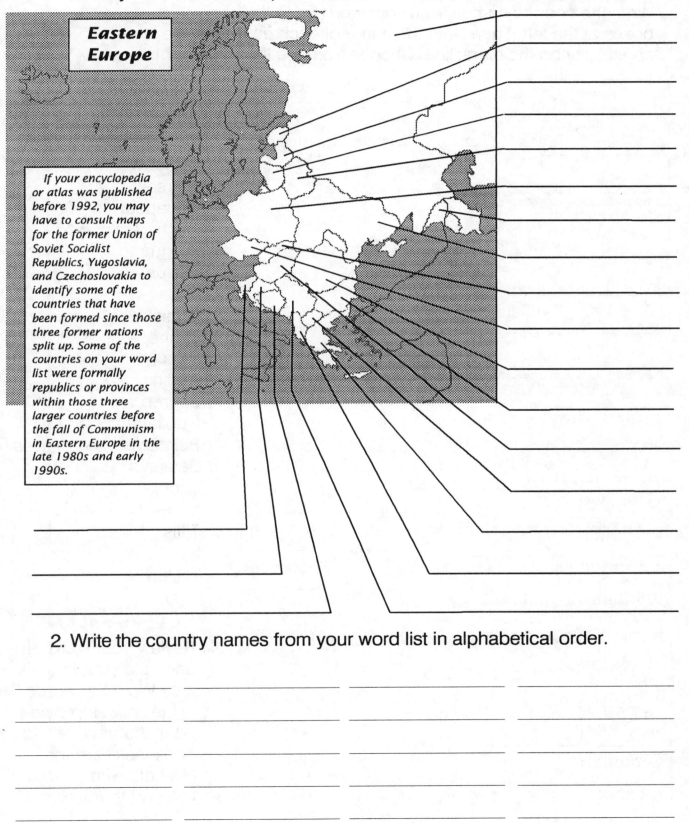

Eastern Europe

If your encyclopedia or atlas was published before 1992, you may have to consult maps for the former Union of Soviet Socialist Republics, Yugoslavia, and Czechoslovakia to identify some of the countries that have been formed since those three former nations split up. Some of the countries on your word list were formally republics or provinces within those three larger countries before the fall of Communism in Eastern Europe in the late 1980s and early 1990s.

2. Write the country names from your word list in alphabetical order.

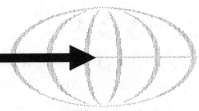

Write the country names from your word list in the boxes at the left. Then write the name of each country's capital city on the blank line. Choose from the list at the right.

Capitals

Moscow
Warsaw
Budapest
Bucharest
Prague
Vilnius
Sofia
Bratislava
Tiranë
Riga
Athens
Zagreb
Ljubljana
Belgrade
Sarajevo
Skopje
Minsk
Tiflis
Kiev
Tallinn

LESSON 5

Review your word list and take your final test. Write the words in the spaces provided at the back of this book. Ask God for His help with your test and thank Him.

UNIT 4

COUNTRIES OF ASIA

India	Australia
China	Malaysia
Japan	Mongolia
Vietnam	Indonesia
North Korea	New Zealand
South Korea	The Philippines
Cambodia	Afghanistan
Thailand	Sri Lanka
Taiwan	Pakistan
Burma	Laos

LESSON 1

Study these list words, using the study plan on page 7.

LESSON 2

Below are adjectives used to describe things related to each of the countries on your word list. In most cases, these words are also the names of the natives and languages of these countries. Learn to spell the words and write them.

Indian	_____	**Malaysian**	_____
Chinese	_____	**Mongolian**	_____
Japanese	_____	**Indonesian**	_____
Vietnamese	_____	**New Zealand***	_____
Korean	_____	**Philippine***	_____
Cambodian	_____	**Afghan**	_____
Thai	_____	**Sri Lankan**	_____
Taiwanese	_____	**Pakistani**	_____
Burmese	_____	**Laotian**	_____
Australian	_____		

> * Natives of New Zealand are called New Zealanders. Natives of The Philippines are called Filipinos.

17

LESSON 3

1. Using an encyclopedia, atlas, or the map on page 129, if necessary, identify the countries of Asia and Oceania indicated below with list words.

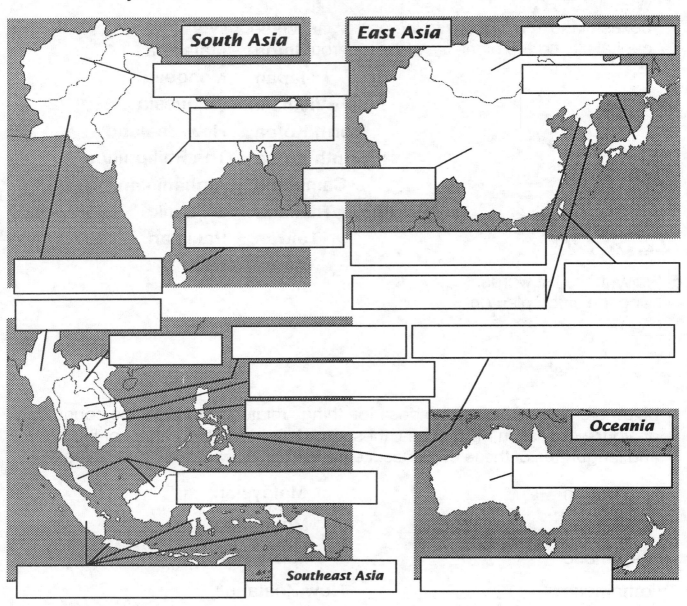

2. Write the country names from your word list in alphabetical order.

_____ _____ _____ _____

_____ _____ _____ _____

_____ _____ _____ _____

_____ _____ _____ _____

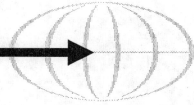

Write the country names from your word list in the boxes at the left. Then write the name of each country's capital city on the blank line. Choose from the list at the right.

Capitals

New Delhi
Beijing
Tokyo
Hanoi
Pyongyang
Seoul
Phnom Penh
Bangkok
Taipei
Rangoon
Canberra
Kuala Lumpur
Ulan Bator
Jakarta
Wellington
Manila
Kabul
Colombo
Islamabad
Vientiane

LESSON 5

Review your word list and take your final test. Write the words in the spaces provided at the back of this book. Ask God for His help with your test and thank Him.

UNIT 5

COUNTRIES OF AFRICA

LESSON 1

Study these list words, using the study plan on page 7.

Chad   Angola
Sudan   Malawi
Nigeria   Zambia
Somalia   Namibia
Ivory Coast   South Africa
Ethiopia   Mozambique
Uganda   Madagascar
Kenya   Zimbabwe
Congo   Tanzania
Zaire   Ghana

LESSON 2

Below are the names of some other countries in Africa. Although you will not be tested on these names, learn to spell them along with the names of the countries on your word list.

Mali _____

Gabon _____

Cameroon _____

Liberia _____

Sierra Leone _____

Guinea _____

Senegal _____

Mauritania _____

The Gambia _____

Morocco _____

Algeria _____

Tunisia _____

Niger _____

Burkina Faso _____

Togo _____

Benin _____

Central African Republic _____

Botswana _____

Rwanda _____

Burundi _____

LESSON 3

1. Using an encyclopedia, atlas, or the map on page 130, if necessary, identify the African countries indicated below with list words.

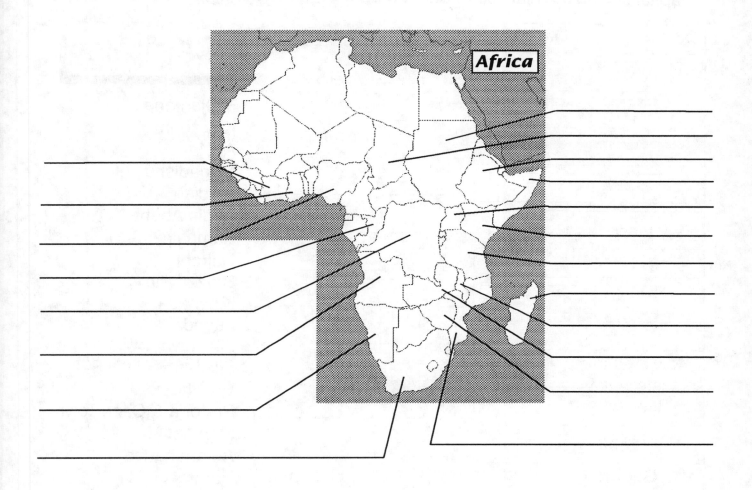

2. Write the country names from your word list in alphabetical order.

_____ _____ _____ _____

_____ _____ _____ _____

_____ _____ _____ _____

_____ _____ _____ _____

_____ _____ _____ _____

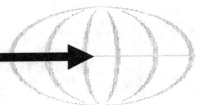

Write the country names from your word list in the boxes at the left. Then write the name of each country's capital city on the blank line. Choose from the list at the right.

Capitals

N'Djamena
Khartoum
Abuja
Mogadishu
Abidjan
Addis Ababa
Kampala
Nairobi
Brazzaville
Kinshasa
Luanda
Lilongwe
Lusaka
Windhoek
Pretoria & Cape Town
Maputo
Antananarivo
Harare
Dar es Salaam
Accra

LESSON 5

Review your word list and take your final test. Write the words in the spaces provided at the back of this book. Ask God for His help with your test and thank Him.

UNIT 6

COUNTRIES OF THE MIDDLE EAST & NORTH AFRICA

Iraq	Libya
Syria	Egypt
Israel	Oman
Jordan	Lebanon
Saudi Arabia	United Arab Emirates
Cyprus	Morocco
Turkey	Tunisia
Kuwait	Algeria
Yemen	Crete
Qatar	Iran

LESSON 1

Study these list words, using the study plan on page 7.

LESSON 2

The Middle East is sometimes called "The Cradle of Civilization," because human history began there. In the Bible you will find ancient names of many of the places in the Middle East whose names have since changed. Write these:

Judea _____   Phoenicia _____

Galilee _____   Bashan _____

Samaria _____   Gilead _____

Canaan _____   Philistia _____

Moab _____   Ammon _____

Edom _____   Sinai _____

Decapolis _____   Asia Minor _____

Assyria _____   Goshen _____

Babylonia _____   Media _____

Persia _____   Mesopotamia _____

LESSON 3

1. Using an encyclopedia, atlas, or the map on page 131, if necessary, identify the Middle Eastern and North African countries shown below with list words.

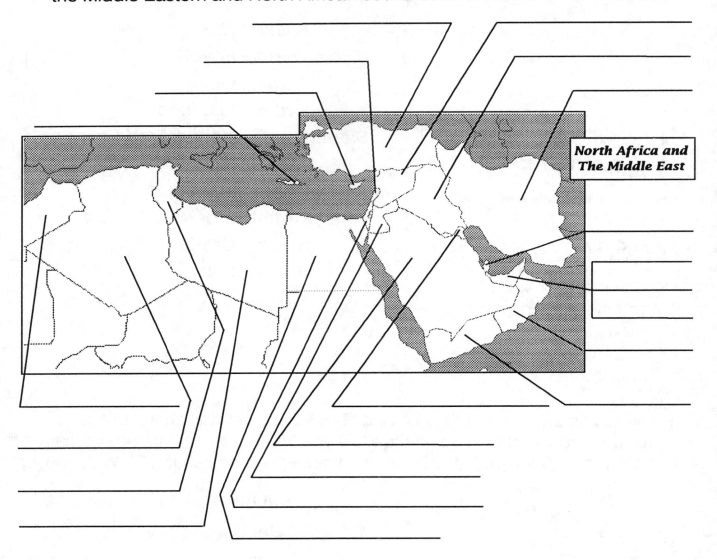

North Africa and
The Middle East

2. Write the place names from your word list in alphabetical order.

_____ _____ _____ _____

_____ _____ _____ _____

_____ _____ _____ _____

_____ _____ _____ _____

_____ _____ _____ _____

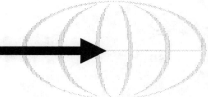

Write the country names from your word list in the boxes at the left. Then write the name of each country's capital city on the blank line. Choose from the list at the right.

Capitals

Baghdad
Damascus
Jerusalem
Amman
Riyadh
Nicosia
Ankara
Kuwait City
San'a
Doha
Tripoli
Cairo
Muscat
Beirut
Abu Dhabi
Rabat
Tunis
Algiers
Athens (Greece)*
Tehran

* Crete is part of Greece, whose capital is Athens.

LESSON 5

Review your word list and take your final test. Write the words in the spaces provided at the back of this book. Ask God for His help with your test and His blessing on your country.

UNIT 7

EASTERN UNITED STATES

LESSON 1

Study these list words, using the study plan on page 7.

LESSON 2

Ohio   Georgia
Maine   Michigan
Florida   Maryland
Indiana   New York
Pennsylvania   New Jersey
Massachusetts New Hampshire
Rhode Island   South Carolina
Connecticut   North Carolina
Delaware   West Virginia
Alabama   Mississippi
Virginia   Tennessee
Illinois   Kentucky
        Vermont

Write the names of the Eastern States from your word list in alphabetical order.

_____   _____   _____

_____   _____   _____

_____   _____   _____

_____   _____   _____

_____   _____   _____

_____   _____   _____

_____   _____   _____

_____

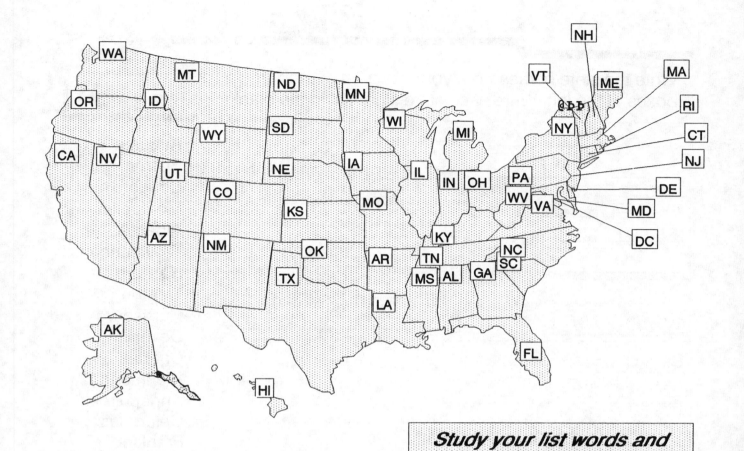

LESSON 3

Study your list words and take a practice test after completing Lesson 3.

1. Using an encyclopedia or atlas, if necessary, match each state from the Eastern and Midwestern portion of the United States with their postal abbreviations indicated below.

ME _____

MA _____	**DE** _____	**NC** _____
NH _____	**WV** _____	**SC** _____
VT _____	**VA** _____	**GA** _____
NY _____	**MD** _____	**AL** _____
RI _____	**OH** _____	**FL** _____
CT _____	**KY** _____	**MI** _____
NJ _____	**TN** _____	**IN** _____
PA _____	**MS** _____	**IL** _____

Write the state names from your word list in the boxes at the left. Write each state's capital in the blank.

Capitals

Augusta
Boston
Concord
Montpelier
Albany
Providence
Hartford
Trenton
Harrisburg
Dover
Charleston
Richmond
Annapolis
Columbus
Frankfort
Nashville
Jackson
Raleigh
Columbia
Atlanta
Montgomery
Tallahassee
Lansing
Indianapolis
Springfield

LESSON 5

Review your word list and take your final test. Write the words in the spaces provided at the back of this book. Ask God for His help with your test. Remember your country in prayer, too.

U*NIT 8*

WESTERN UNITED STATES

LESSON 1

Study these list words, using the study plan on page 7.

LESSON 2

Write the names of the Western States from your word list in alphabetical order.

Iowa   Kansas
Utah   Oregon
Alaska   Nebraska
Hawaii   Wisconsin
Nevada   Minnesota
North Dakota New Mexico
South Dakota Washington
Oklahoma   Louisiana
California   Arkansas
Montana   Colorado
Arizona   Missouri
Idaho   Texas
Wyoming

_____ _____ _____

_____ _____ _____

_____ _____ _____

_____ _____ _____

_____ _____ _____

_____ _____ _____

_____ _____ _____

_____

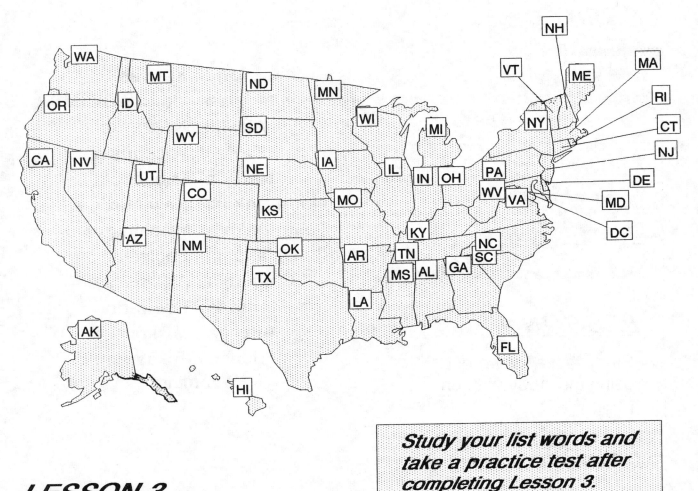

LESSON 3

Study your list words and take a practice test after completing Lesson 3.

1. Using an encyclopedia or atlas to help you, if necessary, match each state from the Western and Midwestern portion of the United States with their postal abbreviations indicated below.

WA _____

MT _____	CA _____	TX _____
ND _____	NV _____	OK _____
MN _____	UT _____	AR _____
WI _____	NE _____	LA _____
OR _____	MO _____	AK _____
ID _____	KS _____	HI _____
WY _____	AZ _____	SD _____
IA _____	NM _____	CO _____

Write the state names from your word list in the boxes at the left. Write each state's capital in the blank.

Capitals

Olympia
Helena
Bismarck
St. Paul
Madison
Salem
Boise
Cheyenne
Des Moines
Sacramento
Carson City
Salt Lake City
Lincoln
Jefferson City
Topeka
Phoenix
Santa Fe
Austin
Oklahoma City
Little Rock
Baton Rouge
Juneau
Honolulu
Pierre
Denver

LESSON 5

Review your word list and take your final test. Write the words in the spaces provided at the back of this book. Ask God for His help with your test. Pray for your state leaders, too.

UNIT 9

THE WORLD OF ASTRONOMY

LESSON 1

Study these list words, using the study plan on page 7.

LESSON 2

Mars	pulsar
Earth	quasar
Venus	meteor
Jupiter	planetarium
Mercury	observatory
Neptune	constellation
Uranus	astronomy
Saturn	astrology
Pluto	telescope
comet	galaxy

1. Write the names of the planets of our solar system.

_____

_____

_____

_____

_____

_____

2. Write two list words referring to groupings of heavenly bodies.

_____

3. Write two list words refering to buildings used to study the heavens.

_____

4. Which list word names a scientific instrument used in astronomy?

_____

5. Write four list words that name heavenly bodies other than those you named in Questions 1 & 2.

_____

_____

_____

6. Write two list words describing studies of the stars.

_____

LESSON 3

1. Look up the word "astronomy" in a dictionary. Write the word and a brief definition.

    _____

    ----

2. Write the names of the planets of our solar system in the order of their orbits around the Sun. Consult an encyclopedia , if necessary.

Sun

3. Write Psalm 8:3-4: _____

    _____

    _____

4. Write: **planetarium** and **observatory.** In the boxes, write the letter of the definition that best fits each word.

    _____ [ ]   A. A building, usually equipped with a telescope, used for viewing actual heavenly bodies.

    _____ [ ]   B. A room or building containing a projector for displaying images of heavenly bodies onto a domed ceiling.

5. Look up | MILKY WAY | in an encyclopedia or dictionary. Which list word fits the description of the Milky Way?

   constellation . galaxy . quasar . pulsar . meteor . comet

   _____

> *Study your list words and take a practice test after completing Lesson 3.*

1. Look up the word "astrology" in a dictionary. Write the word and a brief definition.

_____

_____

_____

2. Write Jeremiah 10:2: _____

_____

_____

3. A certain zone in the night sky contains 12 constellations that are studied by both astronomers and astrologers. This zone is called the Zodiac. Astrologers believe, wrongly, that these constellations have special (magical) ability to direct the lives of people on Earth. Below are symbols of the Zodiac. Try to match the symbols to their astrological names.

Aries (Ram)
Taurus (Bull)
Gemini (Twins)
Cancer (Crab)
Leo (Lion)
Virgo (Virgin)
Libra (Balance Scales)
Scorpio (Scorpion)
Sagittarius (Archer)
Capricorn (Goat)
Aquarius (Water-Bearer)
Pisces (Fish)

_____ _____ _____

_____ _____ _____

_____ _____ _____

_____ _____ _____

LESSON 5

Review your word list and take your final test. Write the words in the spaces provided at the back of this book. Ask God for His help with your test. Praise God for His handiwork in the sky.

UNIT 10

THE WORLD OF FLOWERS

tulip	iris
daisy	aster
pansy	poppy
marigold	primrose
dandelion	honeysuckle
snowdrop	buttercup
sunflower	petunia
bluebell	daffodil
crocus	cowslip
violet	zinnia

LESSON 1

Study these list words, using the study plan on page 7.

LESSON 2

1. A compound word is a word made up of two or more words. Seven of the flower names on your word list are compound words. Write them below.

_____

_____

_____

_____

_____

_____

2. Draw a slash-line (/) between the two words in the compound names of the flowers you have written in Exercise 1.

3. Write the plural form of a list word in the blank in this familiar verse.

> "Roses are red;
>
> _____ are blue.
>
> Sugar is sweet,
>
> and so are you."

4. Below are the titles of some old songs with flowers names. Write the flower names in the blanks.

"Tiptoe Through the Tulips"

_____

"My Little Buttercup"

_____

"Primrose Lane"

_____

"The Bluebells of Scotland"

_____

"Lonely Little Petunia"

_____

LESSON 3

1. Learn these rules for making plurals of nouns.

> A. The plural of most nouns is formed by adding "-s."
> B. Nouns ending with silent -e form their plurals by adding "-s."
> C. The plural of nouns ending with -s, -z, -x, -ch, or -sh is usually formed by adding "-es."
> D. Nouns ending with -y preceded by a consonant form their plurals by changing the "y" to "i" and adding "-es."

2. Write the plural form of all the flower names on your word list. Use the rules in the box above to guide you.

_____   _____   _____   _____

_____   _____   _____   _____

_____   _____   _____   _____

_____   _____   _____   _____

_____   _____   _____   _____

3. Write your list words in alphabetical order. Fill in the blanks below, starting with the left column and moving downward in each column.

_____   _____   _____   _____

_____   _____   _____   _____

_____   _____   _____   _____

_____   _____   _____   _____

_____   _____   _____   _____

Study your list words and take a practice test after completing Lesson 3.

36

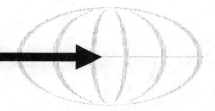

1. Write all your list words three times on a separate sheet of paper.

2. Write Isaiah 40:8 (KJV).

_____

_____

3. Unscramble these flower names to form list words.

sponorwd _____

pubutctre _____

sruenwfol _____

paeitnu _____

bbeeulll _____

ddaiolff _____

cocsur _____

pliswoc _____

levito _____

nizian _____

pulit _____

riis _____

stare _____

yoppp _____

serompir _____

siday _____

snapy _____

glarmido _____

aneldidon _____

clunkseehoy _____

4. Which flower do you see in this picture? Which country from your Unit 2 word list is famous for these?

Flower: _____

Country: _____

_____

5. Which state from your Unit 8 word list does this flower picture remind you of?

State: _____

LESSON 5

Review your word list and take your final test. Write the words in the spaces provided at the back of this book. Ask God for His help with your test. Praise Him for the beauty of flowers.

UNIT 11

THE WORLD OF MUSIC

lyre	lute
harp	piano
tenor	cornet
cymbals	trumpet
accordion	soprano
saxophone	harmony
bagpipe	melody
clarinet	guitar
bugle	violin
alto	bass

LESSON 1

Study these list words, using the study plan on page 7.

LESSON 2

1. Write the names of five musical instruments on your word list that have strings played by plucking, strumming, or stroking with a bow.

_____
_____
_____
_____
_____

2. Write the names of two instruments that have keyboards.

_____
_____

3. Two groups of musical instruments, "winds" and "brass," are played by blowing with the human breath. Write the names of six such instruments, using list words.

_____
_____
_____
_____
_____
_____

4. Which instrument is struck together in pairs or with a stick?

_____

5. Choral music is usually written in four main parts for human voices:

*High female=soprano
Low female=alto
High male=tenor
Low male=bass*

Write the names of these four voice parts:

_____
_____
_____
_____

LESSON 3

1. Review the first four rules for making plurals of nouns. Learn the new one (E).

> A. The plural of most nouns is formed by adding "-s."
> B. Nouns ending with silent -e form their plurals by adding "-s."
> C. The plural of nouns ending with -s, -z, -x, -ch, or -sh is usually formed by adding "-es."
> D. Nouns ending with -y preceded by a consonant form their plurals by changing the "y" to "i" and adding "-es."
> E. Nouns ending with -o preceded by a vowel form their plurals by adding "-s." Most nouns ending with "-o" preceded by a consonant form their plurals by adding "-s." A few need "-es." Check your dictionary to be sure.

2. Write the plural form of all the nouns on your word list. Use the rules in the box above and a dictionary, if necessary, to guide you.

_____ _____ _____ _____

_____ _____ _____ _____

_____ _____ _____ _____

_____ _____ _____ _____

3. Write your list words in alphabetical order. Fill in the blanks below, starting with the left column and moving downward in each column.

_____ _____ _____ _____

_____ _____ _____ _____

_____ _____ _____ _____

_____ _____ _____ _____

_____ _____ _____ _____

Name the instruments shown
←—————— at the left.

Study your list words and take a practice test after completing Lesson 3.

_____ _____ _____ _____

39

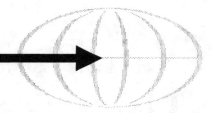

1. Write all your list words three times on a separate sheet of paper.

2. Write Ephesians 5:19 (King James Version). Circle a list word in the verse.

3. Read Psalm 150. Use several different translations, if you have them. Write the names of as many musical instruments as you can find in various versions of this psalm. (You may have more blanks below than needed.)

4. Homonyms are words that have the same or a similar pronounciation but are different in meaning and spelling. Write list words that are homonyms for the following words:

liar _____

loot _____

base _____

symbols _____

5. Write the words below. Look them up in a dictionary and write brief definitions.

melody _____ _____

_____

_____

harmony _____ _____

_____

_____

LESSON 5

Review your word list and take your final test. Write the words in the spaces provided at the back of this book. Ask God for His help with your test. Praise Him with music and for music.

Name this instrument.

_____

UNIT 12

THE WORLD OF BUSINESS

debtor	invoice
creditor	interest
company	customer
corporation	inventory
incorporated	proprietor
merchandise	discount
receivable	balance
payable	receipt
account	capital
amount	ledger

LESSON 1

Study these list words, using the study plan on page 7.

LESSON 2

1. Write the missing letters in these list words. Choose 'or' or 'er.'

debt __ __

credit __ __

propriet __ __

custom __ __

ledg __ __

invent __ __ y

c__ __p__ __ation

inc__ __p__ __ated

int __ __ est

m __ __ chandise

2. Look up the word **'capital'** in a dictionary. Write at least five different definitions for this word. Put a (✔) in the box for every definition related to business.

☐ 1. _____

_____

_____

☐ 2. _____

_____

_____

☐ 3. _____

_____

_____

☐ 4. _____

_____

_____

☐ 5. _____

_____

_____

41

LESSON 3

1. Write your list words. Match them to their meanings by writing the letter of the correct definition in the box next to the word.

debtor	
creditor	
company	
corporation	
incorporated	
merchandise	
receivable	
payable	
account	
amount	
invoice	
interest	
customer	
inventory	
proprietor	
discount	
balance	
receipt	
capital	
ledger	

a. Goods that may be bought or sold
b. A reduction from the standard price or full amount of debt
c. Waiting for payment to be received; capable of being accepted.
d. Amount that remains in an account
e. Due; waiting to be paid out
f. A written statement that a debt payment has been received
g. A record or computation of business actions or payments
h. Money used in a business to build or expand the business
i. A sum; the total number
j. A book or sheet for keeping records of payments or debts
k. One who owes a debt
l. One to whom a debt is owed
m. A written statement that a debt payment is due; a bill
n. Money paid or owed for the use of borrowed or loaned money
o. A group of people; a business organization
p. A group of people legally authorized to act as a single body
q. One who buys goods or services from a business
r. A supply or list of merchandise to be sold by a business
s. Combined into a unified whole or body
t. The owner of a business or piece of property

2. Write your list words in alphabetical order. Fill in the blanks below, starting with the left column and moving downward in each column.

_____   _____   _____

_____   _____   _____

_____   _____   _____

_____   _____   _____

_____   _____   _____

Study your list and take a practice test after completing Lesson 3.

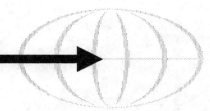

1. Write all your list words three times on a separate sheet of paper.

2. Write 2 Thessalonians 3:12 (KJV).

> _____
>
> _____
>
> _____

3. Write list words to fit these abbreviations of business terms:

Co. _____

Corp. _____

Inc. _____

Acct. _____

Bal. _____

Amt. _____

Mdse. _____

Int. _____

Disc. _____

4. Think up names for three new businesses. Use one of these three list words in each of your business names:

Company

_____

Corporation

_____

Incorporated

_____

5. Write the words in dark type that you find on these business forms. (Use the blank lines.)

LEDGER _____

Accounts receivable:	**Accounts payable:**
_____	_____
_____	_____

Capital Merchandise Corporation

_____

INVOICE _____   **Account** No. _____

Customer _____

Jim Roberts

  Item: Plastics Widgets

  Quantity: 400

  Price: $1 each

Amount _____	$400
Discount _____	-50
Interest _____	+6
Balance _____	$356

RECEIPT _____

Received from Jim Roberts: $356 on **Account**

_____

LESSON 5

Review your word list and take your final test. Write the words in the spaces provided at the back of this book. Ask God for His help with your test.

UNIT 13

TERMS USED IN GEOGRAPHY

gulf   plain
strait   ocean
steppe   tropics
plateau   isthmus
boundary   geography
peninsula   meridians
continent   longitude
equator   parallels
torrid   latitude
frigid   island

LESSON 1

Study these list words, using the study plan on page 7.

LESSON 2

1. Write these words. Then write list words that are homonyms for these words.

golf _____

_____

straight _____

_____

plane _____

_____

step _____

_____

2. Synonyms are words that have the same or similar meanings. Write these list words that have similar meanings.

a. Imaginary circles on the surface of the earth running in the same direction as the equator and marking degrees of distances north and south of the equator.

parallels   **latitude**

_____   _____

b. Imaginary circles on the surface of the earth crossing the equator and passing through the earth's poles and marking east and west distances.

meridians   **longitude**

_____   _____

c. Vast region of level, mostly treeless grassland.

plain _____

steppe _____

parallel (line of latitude)

equator

meridian
(line of longitude)

44

LESSON 3

1. Write the list words in parentheses identifying geographical features of the world.

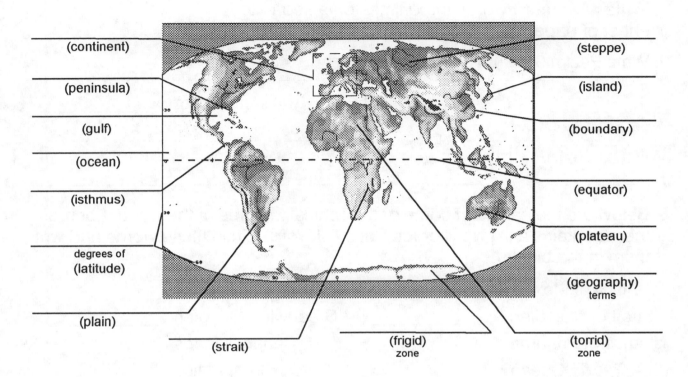

(continent)   (steppe)

(peninsula)   (island)

(gulf)   (boundary)

(ocean)   (equator)

(isthmus)

degrees of (latitude)   (plateau)

(geography) terms

(plain)

(strait)   (frigid) zone   (torrid) zone

2. Antonyms are words with opposite meanings. Write these two antonyms.

    torrid (hot)_____   **frigid (cold)**_____

3. Write your list words in alphabetical order. Fill in the blanks below, starting with the left column and moving downward in each column.

_____   _____   _____   _____

_____   _____   _____   _____

_____   _____   _____   _____

_____   _____   _____   _____

_____   _____   _____   _____

Study your word list and take a practice test after completing Lesson 3.

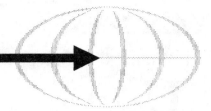

1. Write all your list words three times on a separate sheet of paper.

2. Write Psalm 90:2 (KJV).

_____

_____

_____

3. Below are the names of some geographical features of the world. Each of them contains a list word or form of a list word. Circle these words and write them in the blanks.

Gulf of Mexico _____   The Equator _____

Strait of Magellan _____   Greenwich Meridian _____

Isthmus of Panama _____   Canary Islands _____

Pacific Ocean _____   Great Plains _____

Tropic of Cancer _____   Boundary Peak _____

Steppes of Asia _____   Atlantic Ocean _____

Columbia Plateau _____   Strait of Gibraltar _____

Continent of Asia _____   Tropic of Capricorn _____

Sinai Peninsula _____   Persian Gulf _____

The 49th Parallel _____   Siberian Plain _____

4. Learn the meaning of these list words.

isthmus - a narrow strip of land connecting two larger land areas.
peninsula - a long, narrow area of land surrounded on three sides by water.
strait - a narrow passage of water connecting two larger bodies of water
tropics - the Torrid Zone between the parallels known as the Tropic of Cancer and Tropic of Capricorn.
island - a land mass, usually smaller than a continent, surrounded by water.
continent - any of the seven main land masses of the Earth: Africa, Antarctica, Asia, Australia, Europe, North America, and South America.
gulf - a large area of an ocean or sea partially enclosed by land.

LESSON 5

Review your word list and take your final test. Write the words in the spaces provided at the back of this book. Ask God for His help with your test.

UNIT 14

THE WORLD OF BIRDS

robin	quail
eagle	flicker
oriole	turkey
sparrow	cardinal
pheasant	chickadee
warbler	grosbeak
starling	flamingo
pelican	bobolink
falcon	buzzard
wren	pigeon

LESSON 1

Study these list words, using the study plan on page 7.

LESSON 2

1. Write list words that have spellings similar to these words. Take note of the differences.

pleasant

_____

startling

_____

blizzard

_____

turnkey

_____

---

america's symbol

When God made the oyster, He guaranteed his absolute economic and social security. He built the oyster a house, his shell, to shelter and protect him from his enemies. When hungry, the oyster simply opens his shell and food rushes in for him. He has Freedom from want. But when God made the eagle, He declared, "The blue sky is the limit – build your own house!" So the eagle built on the highest mountain. Storms threaten him every day. For food he flies through miles of rain and snow and wind. The eagle, not the oyster, is the emblem of America.

American Communications Network, quoted in "The Family Album" (Valley Forge, Penn. copyright 1975)

Write: eagle _____

47

LESSON 3

1. Write the names of the birds on your word list in the appropriate columns.

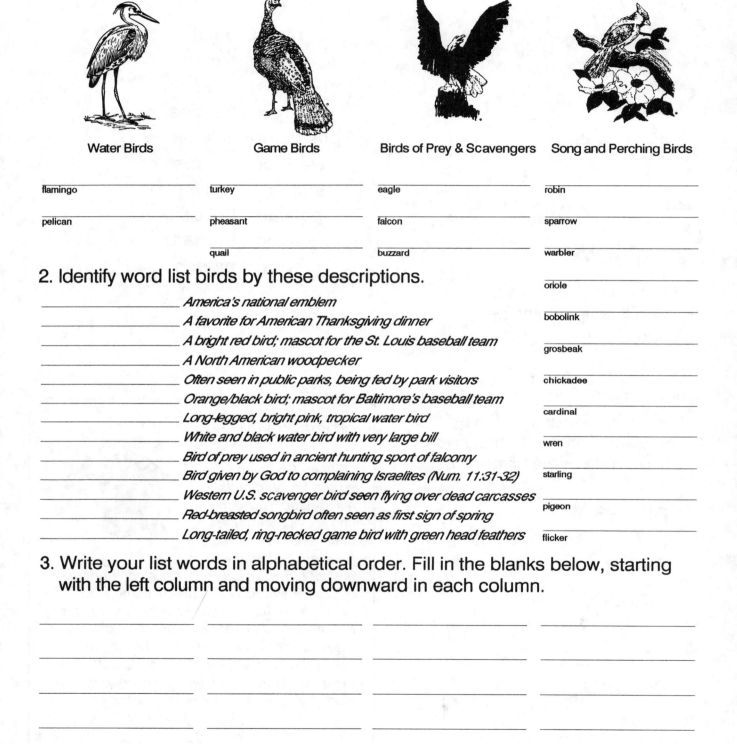

| Water Birds | Game Birds | Birds of Prey & Scavengers | Song and Perching Birds |

flamingo _____ turkey _____ eagle _____ robin _____

pelican _____ pheasant _____ falcon _____ sparrow _____

quail _____ buzzard _____ warbler _____

oriole _____

2. Identify word list birds by these descriptions.

bobolink _____

_____ *America's national emblem*

_____ *A favorite for American Thanksgiving dinner*   grosbeak _____

_____ *A bright red bird; mascot for the St. Louis baseball team*

_____ *A North American woodpecker*   chickadee _____

_____ *Often seen in public parks, being fed by park visitors*

_____ *Orange/black bird; mascot for Baltimore's baseball team* cardinal _____

_____ *Long-legged, bright pink, tropical water bird*

_____ *White and black water bird with very large bill*   wren _____

_____ *Bird of prey used in ancient hunting sport of falconry*

_____ *Bird given by God to complaining Israelites (Num. 11:31-32)* starling _____

_____ *Western U.S. scavenger bird seen flying over dead carcasses* _____

_____ *Red-breasted songbird often seen as first sign of spring* pigeon _____

_____ *Long-tailed, ring-necked game bird with green head feathers* flicker _____

3. Write your list words in alphabetical order. Fill in the blanks below, starting with the left column and moving downward in each column.

_____   _____   _____   _____

_____   _____   _____   _____

_____   _____   _____   _____

_____   _____   _____   _____

_____   _____   _____   _____

Study your word list. Take a practice test after completing Lesson 3.

48

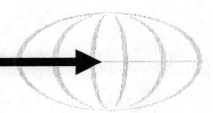

1. Write all your list words three times on a separate sheet of paper.

2. Write Song of Solomon 2:12 (KJV).

_____

_____

_____

3. Complete these list words.

__ __ **zz** __ __ __

__ __ __ **rr** __ __

__ __ __ __ __ __ __ **ee**

e __ __ **e**

o __ __ **o** __

__ **o** __ **o** __ __ __

__ **a** __ __ __ **a** __

__ __ **r** __ __ **r**

b __ **b** __ __ __ __

c __ __ **c** __ __ __ __

__ __ __ **a** __ **a** __ __

4. The 'words' below are combinations of parts of the bird names on your word list. Write the real names of the two birds whose names are included in each combination.

bobobeak { _____

buzzadee { _____

sparling { _____

pigingo { _____

cardican { _____

pheasler { _____

orren { _____

fligle { _____

turcon { _____

quabin { _____

LESSON 5

Review your word list and take your final test. Write the words in the spaces provided at the back of this book. Ask God for His help with your test.

UNIT 15

THE WORLD OF SPORTS

LESSON 1

Study these list words, using the study plan on page 7.

golf   racing
polo   rowing
skiing   cycling
archery   skating
basketball   gymnastics
volleyball   wrestling
baseball   fencing
football   sailing
hockey   boxing
tennis   soccer

LESSON 2

1. Write the names of sports from your word list in which a ball is used.

_____

_____

_____

_____

_____

2. Fill in the blanks with list words.

A. Name a sport played on a 'diamond.' _____

B. Name two sports played on a 'court.' _____

_____

C. Name a sport played on a 'course.' _____

D. Name two sports done on 'water.' _____

_____

E. Name a sport played with a 'racquet.' _____

F. Name two sports that use 'kicking.' _____

_____

G. Name a sport done on 'wheels.' _____

H. Name two sports played on 'ice.' _____

_____

I. Name two sports with 'body contact.' _____

_____

J. Name two sports using 'horses.' _____

_____

K. Name two sports played over 'nets.' _____

_____

L. Name a sport that may be done on either 'snow or water.' _____

M. Name a sport done in a 'gymnasium.' _____

50

LESSON 3
1. Identify these sports with list words.

_____ _____ _____ _____

_____ _____ _____ _____

_____ _____ _____ _____

2. Write your list words in alphabetical order. Fill in the blanks below, starting with the left column and moving downward in each column.

_____	_____	_____	_____
_____	_____	_____	_____
_____	_____	_____	_____
_____	_____	_____	_____
_____	_____	_____	_____

Study your word list. Take a practice test after completing Lesson 3.

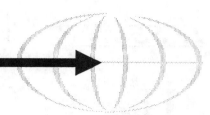
1. Write all your list words three times on a separate sheet of paper.

2. Write 1 Corinthians 9:24 (KJV).

_____

_____

_____

3. Complete these list words.

__ __ __ **ing**

__ __ __ **ing**

__ __ __ **ing**

__ __ __ **ing**

__ __ __ __ **ing**

__ __ __ __ **ing**

__ __ __ __ **ing**

__ __ __ __ **ing**

__ __ __ __ __ __ **ing**

__ __ __ __ **ball**

__ __ __ __ **ball**

__ __ __ __ __ **ball**

__ __ __ __ __ __ **ball**

4. Identify these sports with list words.

_____   _____

_____   _____

5. Of the sports on your word list, name your two favorites.

LESSON 5

_____   _____

Review your word list and take your final test. Write the words in the spaces provided at the back of this book. Ask God for His help with your test.

UNIT 16

KINDS OF BUILDINGS

prison	capitol
temple	mosque
cottage	barracks
mansion	restaurant
tabernacle	skyscraper
courthouse	synagogue
warehouse	monastery
cathedral	dormitory
hospital	foundry
theater	factory

LESSON 1

Study these list words, using the study plan on page 7.

LESSON 2

1. Name six buildings that are used for religious purposes.

_____

_____

_____

_____

_____

2. Name three types of buildings used as dwellings for people.

_____

_____

3. Name a building where you can buy and enjoy a meal.

_____

4. Name a building used as housing for army troops.

_____

5. Name two buildings used for government purposes.

_____

_____

6. Name a building used for jailing criminals.

_____

7. Name a very tall city building usually used for business offices.

_____

8. Name three kinds of buildings used by industries.

_____

_____

_____

9. Name a building used for the care and treatment of the sick.

_____

LESSON 3

1. Identify these buildings with list words.

_____ _____ _____

2. Write three list words that are compound words.

_____ _____ _____

3. Answer these questions with list words.

A. What kind of house might a poor man live in? _____

B. What kind of house might a rich man live in? _____

C. Where might a college student live? _____

D. Where are people accused of crimes taken for trial? _____

E. Where are people who are found guilty of crimes taken for punishment? _____

F. Where might you be taken if you had a serious accident? _____

G. Where does the U.S. Congress hold its lawmaking sessions? _____

H. Where was your father's car built? _____

I. What kind of factory makes things out of iron and steel? _____

J. What kind of building is the famous Empire State Building in New York City? _____

K. Where might your father take your mother for a fine dinner on their anniversary? _____

L. Where might you live if you become a soldier? _____

4. Write your list words in alphabetical order. Fill in the blanks below, starting with the left column and moving downward in each column.

_____ _____ _____ _____

_____ _____ _____ _____

_____ _____ _____ _____

_____ _____ _____ _____

Study your word list. Take a practice test after completing Lesson 3.

54

1. Write all your list words three times on a separate sheet of paper.

2. Write Revelation 21:3 (KJV). Which list word is in this verse?_____

_____

_____

_____

_____

3. Write 1 Corinthians 6:19 (KJV). Which list word is in this verse?_____

_____

_____

_____

_____

4. Which place of worship do you associate with each picture or symbol? Choose from: cathedral, mosque, synagogue, temple or tabernacle.

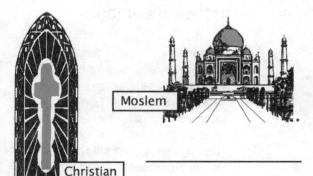

_____   _____   _____

_____

5. Look these words up in a dictionary and write them below. Notice the differences in spelling and meaning.

capitol_____   **capital**_____

LESSON 5

Review your word list and take your final test. Write the words in the spaces provided at the back of this book. Ask God for His help with your test.

U*NIT 17*

THE WORLD OF ANATOMY

LESSON 1

Study these list words, using the study plan on page 7.

vein   artery
thigh   spine
lungs   bronchi
glands   ligament
membrane   intestine
diaphragm   abdomen
appendix   cartilage
muscle   stomach
kidney   tendon
liver   larynx

LESSON 2

1. Write the word: **anatomy.** _____ Look up the word in a dictionary and learn its meaning.

2. Write the names of these parts of the body and learn their meanings.

_____ lungs - sacs in the chest used for the exchange of air for the blood stream

_____ thigh - part of the leg between the knee and the hip

_____ glands - organs that produce and separate out body fluids

_____ spine - the backbone and the large central nerve running through it

_____ larynx - the organ in the neck containing the vocal cords

_____ membrane - a thin layer of tissue covering or separating organs

_____ artery - a vessel that carries blood away from the heart

_____ vein - a vessel that carries blood to the heart

_____ abdomen - the central portion of the trunk of humans' or mammals' body

_____ intestine - a canal carrying digested food and wastes from the stomach

_____ diaphragm - muscle dividing chest and abdomen; used for breathing

_____ kidney - organ that keeps proper water balance in the body

_____ stomach - organ that receives and digests food

_____ cartilage - tough elastic tissue attached to bones at the joints

_____ tendon - tough fiberous tissue attaching muscles to bones

_____ ligament - tough fiberous tissue holding bones or cartilage in place

_____ liver - gland that changes or purifies substances in the blood

_____ muscle - tissue that contracts or relaxes causing bone movement

_____ appendix - a tube on an organ where the large intestine begins

_____ bronchi - the branched tubes that carry air from throat to lungs

56

LESSON 3

1. A suffix is an ending attached to a base word to form another word. The suffix -*itis* means 'a disease' (usually inflammation) of an organ of the body.' Below are the names of four diseases with this suffix. Write the name of the disease. Then, using list words, write the name of the organ affected.

laryngitis _____ = **inflammation of the** _____
bronchitis _____ = **inflammation of the** _____
tendinitis _____ = **inflammation of the** _____
appendicitis _____ = **inflammation of the** _____

NOTE: Tendinitis may also be spelled tendonitis. The preferred spelling above changes the 'o' in tendon to 'i.'

2. The suffix -*al* is added to nouns to form adjectives meaning 'related to,' 'pertaining to,' or 'proceeding from.' Below are the adjective forms of five list words. Write the adjectives and the list words from which they are derived.

spinal _____ = **related to the** _____
arterial _____ = **related to the** _____
intestinal _____ = **related to the** _____
bronchial _____ = **related to the** _____
abdominal _____ = **related to the** _____

Notice the change in the spelling of 'abdomen' that you must make before adding the suffix to spell 'abdominal.'

3. The suffix -*ar* is added to nouns to form adjectives meaning 'related to,' 'pertaining to,' or 'proceeding from.' Below are the adjective forms of two list words. Write the adjectives and the list words from which they are derived.

muscular _____ = **related to the** _____
glandular _____ = **related to the** _____

Notice the change in the spelling of 'muscle' that you must make before adding the suffix. The letters 'ul' in both of these words come from the Latin root words, *muscula* and *glandula,* from which the words are derived.

4. Write your list words in alphabetical order. Fill in the blanks below, starting with the left column and moving downward in each column.

_____ _____ _____ _____

_____ _____ _____ _____

_____ _____ _____ _____

_____ _____ _____ _____

_____ _____ _____ _____

Study your word list. Take a practice test after completing Lesson 3.

1. Write all your list words three times on a separate sheet of paper.

2. Read 1 Corinthians 15:42-53 (KJV). Write verse 44 below.

> _____
>
> _____
>
> _____

3. The list word 'bronchi' is plural, although it does not follow any of the usual rules of spelling for plural English words. The singular form of this word is 'bronchus.' The root of this word is 'bronchos,' a Greek word meaning 'throat.' The singular (-us) and plural (-i) endings for our present word are taken directly from Latin, the language of the ancient Romans. Write both forms.

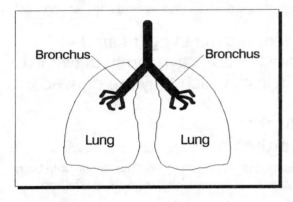

bronchus_____

bronchi_____

4. The plural of 'appendix' is 'appendices.' Notice that the 'x' is changed to 'c' before the plural ending 'es' is added. The correct full name of the body organ which we call the 'appendix' is actually 'vermiform appendix.' Look up the word 'appendix' in a dictionary and write at least one <u>other</u> definition in the box below. Write the word and its plural form.

appendix_____

appendices_____

Definition

LESSON 5

Review your word list and take your final test. Write the words in the spaces provided at the back of this book. Ask God for His help with your test.

UNIT 18

FORMS AND OFFICES OF GOVERNMENT

empire   kingdom
republic   embassy
monarchy   theocracy
democracy   representative
dictatorship   commonwealth
aristocracy   congressman
presidency   ambassador
anarchy   legislature
minister   secretary
senator   legislator

LESSON 1

Study these list words, using the study plan on page 7.

LESSON 2

1. Write the word: **government.** _____ Look up the word in a dictionary and learn its meaning.

2. The suffix '-cracy' comes from the Latin '-cratia' and Greek '-kratia,' which come in turn from the Greek word 'kratos,' meaning 'power' or 'strength.' The suffix '-archy' comes from the Latin '-archia' and Greek 'arches,' meaning 'rule' or 'government.' Using these two suffixes, along with the prefixes discussed in the box, write list words from the clues below.

These prefixes also have Greek and Latin origins:

aristo-: refers to the upper class, wealthy, or best people in a society.

demo-: refers to the common people or mass of people.

theo-: refers to God.

a- or an-: mean 'no' or nothing.

mon- or mono-: refer to 'one.'

Power or government by God: _____

No government or ruling order: _____

Power by the people: _____

Power by the privileged class: _____

Rule by one person: _____

LESSON 3

1. Learn the meanings of the forms of government listed below and write the words.

empire _____ { An extended group of nations ruled by a single power.

republic _____ { A state or nation ruled by representatives elected by the citizens.

kingdom _____ { A nation ruled by a king or queen.

dictatorship _____ { A nation or territory ruled by a person with total and absolute power in himself.

commonwealth _____ { An association of self-governing nations having a common allegiance with a mother country.

2. Say the 'Pledge of Allegiance' to the American flag, either with your class or alone. According to the Pledge, what kind of nation is the United States? The answer is a list word. Write it in the blank below.

"I pledge allegiance to the flag of the United States of America and to the _____ for which it stands: one nation under God, indivisible, with liberty and justice for all."

3. Write these two list words. Look them up in a dictionary and learn the difference in their meanings. They are derived from the Latin word 'lex,' which means 'law.' Can you see the connection between 'lex' and the 'law-making' idea in the definitions of these two list words?

legislature _____   legislator _____

In 1644, Samuel Rutherford wrote a book called "Lex Rex." He intended to show by the title that 'the law is king' or 'the king is under or subject to the law.' This important idea was used by the American Founding Fathers when they wrote the United States Constitution. The writers of the Constitution wanted to form a nation in which people were ruled by law, not by changing ideas of men who may be able to gain power at different times. Isn't it sad that this important Christian idea has become weakened over the years?

4. Write your list words in alphabetical order. Fill in the blanks below, starting with the left column and moving downward in each column.

_____   _____   _____   _____

_____   _____   _____   _____

_____   _____   _____   _____

_____   _____   _____   _____

Study your word list. Take a practice test after completing Lesson 3.

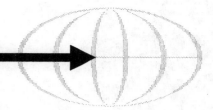

1. Write all your list words three times on a separate sheet of paper.

2. Write Matthew 4:17 (KJV). Which list word is found in this verse?

3. Circle the list words (or forms of them) in these statements. Write the words.

George Washington was the first man to hold the office of the American presidency.

_____

"A wicked messenger falls into trouble, but a faithful ambassador brings health" (Proverbs 13:17, NKJV).

_____

Karl Marx taught that before communism reached perfection, the common class of wage-earners (proletariat) would have to be ruled by a dictatorship.

_____

Daniel Webster, who was both a U.S. representative and senator, once said, "Whatever makes men good Christians, makes them good citizens...."

_____
_____

"A commonwealth...is a...civil society of men, united together to promote their mutual safety and prosperity by means of their union" (Samuel Adams).

_____

The power of the legislature is "to make laws, and not to make legislators" (John Locke).

_____

"The political writers of antiquity will not allow more than three regular forms of government; ...a democracy; ...an aristocracy; [and a] ...monarchy" (William Blakestone).

_____
_____
_____

"[T]here are indications that in every place the society of believers in Christ was a little republic..." (Leonard Bacon).

_____

"Do you want to be unafraid of the authority? Do what is good, and you will have praise from the same. For he is God's minister to you for good" (Romans 13:3b-4a, NKJV).

LESSON 5

Review your word list and take your final test. Write the words in the spaces provided at the back of this book. Ask God for His help with your test.

U*NIT 19*

TITLES FOR CIVIL OFFICERS

mayor	notary
sheriff	auditor
deputy	treasurer
surveyor	alderman
magistrate	supervisor
commissioner	administrator
councilman	inspector
constable	chairman
coroner	assessor
bailiff	governor

LESSON 1

Study these list words, using the study plan on page 7.

LESSON 2

1. Write all list words ending with '-or.'

_____

_____

_____

_____

_____

_____

2. Write all list words ending with '-er.'

_____

_____

_____

3. Write all list words ending with '-man.'

_____

_____

_____

4. Write all list words ending with '-iff.'

_____

_____

5. Write all list words ending with '-ary,' '-ty,' '-able,' and '-ate.'

_____

_____

_____

LESSON 3

1. Write appropriate list words in the blanks.

_____ a. One who inspects (officially examines or reviews)

_____ b. One who assesses (sets values for taxes)

_____ c. One who administers (manages)

_____ d. One who surveys (measures boundries of land parcels)

_____ e. One who supervises (directs activities or programs)

_____ f. One who governs (directs public affairs; rules)

_____ g. One who is a member of a commission (official task group)

_____ h. One who audits (examines or verifies financial records)

_____ i. One who oversees the public treasury (money or funds)

2. Write the names of these civil officers in law enforcement and public justice. Choose one of the words in parentheses below each blank.

_____
(sheriff/supervisor)
a. The highest police officer in a U.S. county

_____
(mayor/deputy)
b. An assistant officer authorized to act for a sheriff

_____
(constable/governor)
c. A peace officer who handles small offenses

_____
(notary/bailiff)
d. An officer who guards prisoners and keeps order in a courtroom

_____
(chairman/magistrate)
e. A minor official with limited authority as a judge

3. A 'notary' (also known as a 'notary public') is a public official whose duty is to witness the signing of documents and certify that the signatures are authentic. Write: **notary** _____

4. Write your list words in alphabetical order. Fill in the blanks below, starting with the left column and moving downward in each column.

_____ _____ _____ _____

_____ _____ _____ _____

_____ _____ _____ _____

_____ _____ _____ _____

_____ _____ _____ _____

Study your word list. Take a practice test after completing Lesson 3.

63

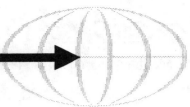

1. Write all your list words three times on a separate sheet of paper.

2. Write Titus 3:1 (KJV).

---

3. LAWMAKERS

In our modern world, laws are usually made by groups of elected officials. At higher levels of government, these groups may be known as the Congress, Parliament, or Legislature. At lower levels of government, laws are usually made by elected groups known as Councils, Commissions, or Boards. Below are some typical names of law-making groups for governments of cities, counties, or parishes in the United States. These names include list words or related forms of list words. Circle the list words (or related words) and write them in the blanks.

City Council _____

Board of Aldermen _____

County Commission _____

Board of Supervisors _____

Town Councilmen _____

City Commissioners _____

> The leader of a council, commission, or board is sometimes called the 'chairman.' He conducts the meetings of the group, appoints members of committees, and fills other leadership roles. Write: **chairman.**
>
> _____

What is the name of the law-making group in your city, town, county, or parish? Ask your parent, teacher, or other adult. Write the name below.

> A 'coroner' is a public official who determines the cause of death of victims of accident or crimes. Write: **coroner.**
>
> _____

_____

4. EXECUTIVES

In most forms of government in democratic countries, there are certain officials who have the responsibility to make sure that the laws written by groups such as those above are carried out or 'executed' as intended. These officials may have many different names. Below are some of them. Write the words printed in dark type.

_____ **mayor** (chief executive of a town or city, usually elected)

_____ **governor** (chief executive of a state or province)

_____ **administrator** (chief manager of a town, city, or department of government)

LESSON 5

> Review your word list and take your final test. Write the words in the spaces provided at the back of this book. Pray for help ... and for all public officials.

UNIT 20

SCIENTIFIC AND TECHNICAL INSTRUMENTS

gauge	receiver
sextant	transmitter
camera	photocopier
telescope	thermometer
microscope	speedometer
seismograph	hydrometer
stethoscope	barometer
generator	facsimile
computer	intercom
compass	amplifier

LESSON 1

Study these list words, using the study plan on page 7.

LESSON 2

1. Write all list words ending with '-meter.'

_____

_____

_____

_____

2. Write all list words ending with '-scope.'

_____

_____

3. Write all list words ending with '-er,' (other than those you wrote in answer 1).

_____

_____

_____

_____

_____

4. Which list word ends with '-or'?

_____

5. Write all list words that have the letter combination 'com.'

_____

_____

_____

6. Write all list words not included in 1-5.

_____

_____

_____

_____

LESSON 3

1. Name these instruments. Choose: stethoscope, microscope, or telescope.

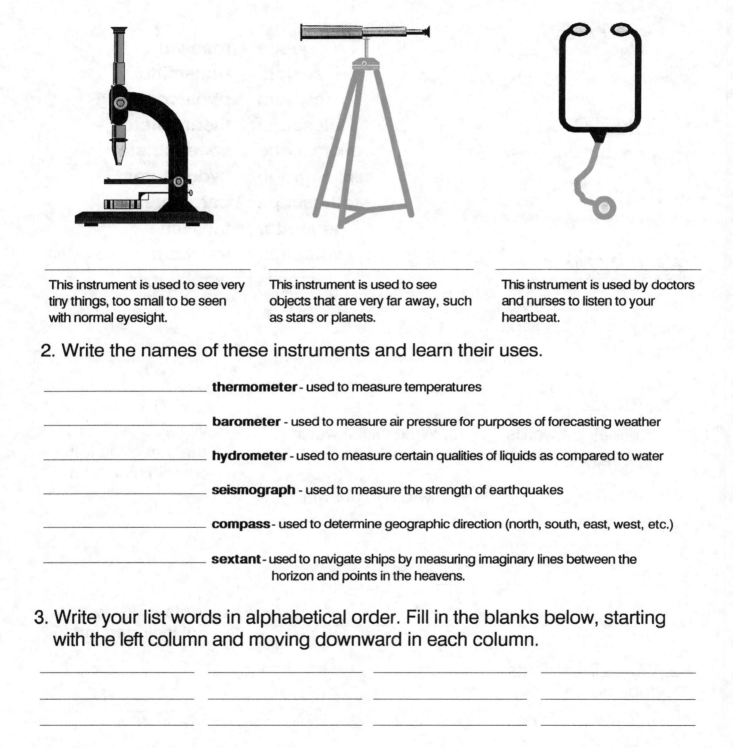

_____

This instrument is used to see very tiny things, too small to be seen with normal eyesight.

_____

This instrument is used to see objects that are very far away, such as stars or planets.

_____

This instrument is used by doctors and nurses to listen to your heartbeat.

2. Write the names of these instruments and learn their uses.

_____ **thermometer** - used to measure temperatures

_____ **barometer** - used to measure air pressure for purposes of forecasting weather

_____ **hydrometer** - used to measure certain qualities of liquids as compared to water

_____ **seismograph** - used to measure the strength of earthquakes

_____ **compass** - used to determine geographic direction (north, south, east, west, etc.)

_____ **sextant** - used to navigate ships by measuring imaginary lines between the horizon and points in the heavens.

3. Write your list words in alphabetical order. Fill in the blanks below, starting with the left column and moving downward in each column.

_____   _____   _____   _____

_____   _____   _____   _____

_____   _____   _____   _____

_____   _____   _____   _____

_____   _____   _____   _____

Study your word list. Take a practice test after completing Lesson 3.

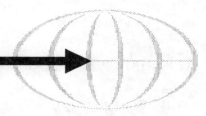

1. Write all your list words three times on a separate sheet of paper.

2. Write Proverbs 16:11(KJV).

3. Write the names of these electronic or electrical instruments. Learn their uses.

_____ **receiver** - a radio, television, or telephone device that receives electrical signals

_____ **transmitter** - a radio, television, or telephone device that sends out electrical signals

_____ **amplifier** - an electronic device used to increase voltage, current, or power

_____ **computer** - an electronic device that performs calculations and processes information

_____ **intercom** - a two-way communications device

_____ **generator** - a machine that changes mechanical energy into electrical energy

4. A 'gauge' is an instrument with a scale or dial used for measurement.
   Write: **gauge.** _____
   Which list word names a gauge used to measure speed?_____

5. Three list words name devices used to make or copy images. Write the words and learn these facts about them.

camera _____
A device for capturing photographic images on film through a lens or lenses.

photocopier _____
A device for copying printed material on paper using a photographic process.

facsimile _____ transmitter-receiver (nickname: FAX)
A machine used to send and receive images over telephone lines.

LESSON 5

Review your word list and take your final test. Write the words in the spaces provided at the back of this book. Ask God for His help with your test.

UNIT 21

THE WORLD OF LAW

jury acquit
libel convict
arson warrant
arrest burglary
subpoena homicide
defendant attorney
plaintiff slander
statute lawyer
felony justice
writ judge

LESSON 1

Study these list words, using the study plan on page 7.

LESSON 2

1. Write: felony.

_____

A felony is any serious crime. Write the names of these three felonies from your word list.

_____

homicide - murder; the killing of a person

_____

burglary - illegal entry of a building with intent to steal

_____

arson - illegal setting of a fire to destroy property

2. Write the two list words in dark print below. Notice the similarities in their meanings.

_____

lawyer - a person trained and qualified to give advice to people about the law and to represent them in court

_____

attorney - a person, especially a lawyer, officially appointed to act on behalf of someone else

3. The three list words in dark print below are names of legal documents. Write the words and learn their meanings.

_____

warrant - a legal document authorizing a search, seizure, or arrest

_____

writ - a written court order commanding a person to do or not to do a certain action

_____

subpoena - a writ ordering the person named in it to appear in court

68

LESSON 3

1. Circle all list words in the following paragraph describing how the criminal justice system works. Write the circled words in the blanks below the paragraph.

The criminal justice system begins to operate when a lawbreaker commits a crime, perhaps a felony such as robbery, homicide, assault, arson, burglary, sale of illegal drugs, or some other violation of a statute (law). The police will try to learn who the criminal is, and they will try to arrest him. If they need evidence to prove he is the one who committed the crime, they may ask a judge for a warrant giving them the right to search his house or other property. When he is arrested, he will have the right to be represented in court by an attorney. He will hire his own lawyer if he can afford one. If he is too poor, the court will appoint one to represent him. The accused criminal will then be brought to trial, during which a jury of his fellow citizens will be asked to decide whether he is guilty or innocent. When a defendant (the person accused of wrong-doing) is found innocent, the court will acquit him. If he is found guilty, the court will convict him of the crime and sentence him to some form of punishment. In a court of law, the person who makes an accusation or complaint is called a plaintiff. In a criminal case, the government fills that role. In order to determine the truth in a legal case, each side may want to call witnesses to testify about what they know. Some witnesses do not want to testify, so the court may issue a writ known as a subpoena to compel them to appear in court and tell what they know.

Some court cases do not involve crimes. Instead, they involve disagreements between individuals or groups. These are called 'civil' cases. An example of such a case might be one in which one party accuses another party of libel (writing something false and damaging about another) or slander (speaking something false and damaging about another).

_____   _____   _____   _____

_____   _____   _____   _____

_____   _____   _____   _____

_____   _____   _____   _____

_____   _____   _____   _____

2. Write your list words in alphabetical order. Fill in the blanks below, starting with the left column and moving downward in each column.

_____   _____   _____   _____

_____   _____   _____   _____

_____   _____   _____   _____

_____   _____   _____   _____

_____   _____   _____   _____

Study your word list. Take a practice test after completing Lesson 3.

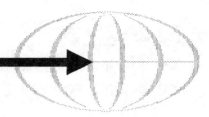

1. Write all your list words three times on a separate sheet of paper.

2. Romans 13:3 (KJV).

3. The phonetic sound 'er' as in 'her' may be spelled 'er,' 'ir,' 'ur,' 'or,' or 'ear.' The following list words are commonly pronounced with this sound. Circle the letters that spell the sound and write the words in the blanks that follow them.

jury _____

burglary _____

attorney _____

lawyer _____

slander _____

4. Look up these two words in a dictionary. Learn the differences in their meanings. Notice the small difference in their spellings. Write the words.

statue _____

statute _____

5. Learn or review these spelling rules for making plurals of words ending with 'y.'

   a. Nouns ending with 'y' preceded by a consonant form their plurals by changing the 'y' to 'i' and adding 'es.' Example: army -> armies.

   b. Nouns ending with 'y' preceded by a vowel usually form their plurals by simply adding 's.' Example: chimney -> chimneys.

Write the plurals of these list words.

jury _____

attorney _____

felony _____

burglary _____

6. Write this list word and learn how to pronounce it.

subpoena _____

sə - pē' - nə   (suh-PEE-nuh)

LESSON 5

Review your word list and take your final test. Write the words in the spaces provided at the back of this book. Ask God for His help with your test.

UNIT 22

THE WORLD OF TREES

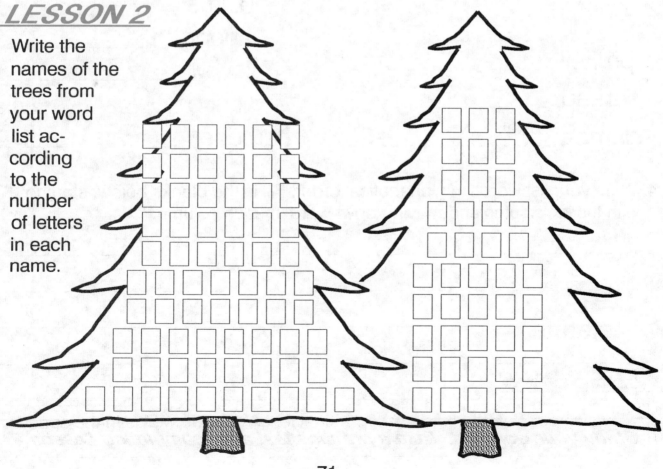

fir oak
elm olive
birch spruce
juniper balsam
cottonwood sycamore
hickory magnolia
aspen walnut
maple poplar
cedar willow
palm pine

LESSON 1

Study these list words, using the study plan on page 7.

LESSON 2

Write the names of the trees from your word list according to the number of letters in each name.

LESSON 3

1. What trees are represented in these pictures? Write: pine, magnolia, or maple.

_____   _____   _____

2. Unscramble the names of these cone-bearing trees.

ceprus _____

epni _____

irf _____

pruneji _____

cread _____

slamba _____

3. Unscramble the names of these leafy trees.

woottoocnd _____

spane _____

palme _____

lappor _____

lowwil _____

chirb _____

marecosy _____

4. Write your list words in alphabetical order. Fill in the blanks below, starting with the left column and moving downward in each column.

_____ _____ _____ _____

_____ _____ _____ _____

_____ _____ _____ _____

_____ _____ _____ _____

_____ _____ _____ _____

Study your word list. Take a practice test after completing Lesson 3.

72

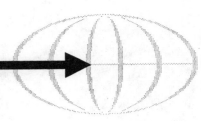

1. Write all your list words three times on a separate sheet of paper.

2. Read Psalm 1 (KJV). Write verse 3 below.

_____

_____

_____

3. Read these verses in the Bible (KJV). Which word-list trees are mentioned?

Isaiah 1:30 _____

I Kings 19:4 _____

Psalm 52:8 _____

Isaiah 60:13 _____

_____

Psalm 137:2 _____

Hosea 4:13 _____

_____

_____

Luke 19:4 _____

Psalm 92:12 _____

_____

"...But only God can make a tree."

(From "Trees," by Joyce Kilmer)

LESSON 5

Review your word list and take your final test. Write the words in the spaces provided at the back of this book. Ask God for His help with your test.

UNIT 23

THE WORLD OF HEALTH

diet	doctor
clinic	healthy
therapy	calories
disease	immunity
ambulance	vaccination
wheelchair	symptoms
aerobics	medicine
exercise	nutrition
vitamin	surgery
nurse	dentist

LESSON 1

Study these list words, using the study plan on page 7.

LESSON 2

1. Which list words name three kinds of people who offer health services?

_____   _____   _____

2. Which list words name two kinds of transportation for sick or injured people?

_____   _____

3. Which four list words are related in some way to the food we eat?

_____   _____   _____   _____

4. Which two list words refer to physical activity designed to keep us healthy?

_____   _____

5. Which list word is the proper medical term for a "shot," an injecttion with a needle to prevent disease?

_____

6. Which list word names a place people go for medical treatment?

_____

7. Which list word means 'illness,' 'sickness,' 'defect,' or 'ailment'?

_____

LESSON 3

1. Match these list words to the pictures at the left.

vaccination

dentist

surgery

diet

aerobics

therapy

wheelchair

ambulance

nurse

_____ _____ _____

2. Write your list words in alphabetical order. Fill in the blanks below, starting with the left column and moving downward in each column.

_____ _____ _____

_____ _____ _____

_____ _____ _____

_____ _____ _____

_____ _____ _____

Study your word list. Take a practice test after completing Lesson 3.

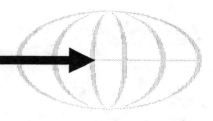

1. Write all your list words three times on a separate sheet of paper.

2. Read Psalm 103:1-6. Write verses 2 and 3 in the box below.

3. Write a list word that is an adjective._____ What is an adjective?

4. Circle the list word at the right that completes the sentence. Write the word.

Jim went to the medical _____ for treatment.

| aerobics |
| immunity |
| clinic |

Oranges are a good source of _____ C.

| exercise |
| vitamin |
| calories |

Eating balanced meals is a key to good _____.

| nutrition |
| surgery |
| disease |

You can buy _____ at a drug store.

| aerobics |
| medicine |
| symptoms |

A runny nose and cough may be_____of a cold.

| therapy |
| vaccination |
| symptoms |

LESSON 5

Review your word list and take your final test. Write the words in the spaces provided at the back of this book. Prayer is a source of help and health.

UNIT 24

THE WORLD OF ECONOMICS

retail   credit
cashier   wealthy
banking   marketing
salesman   checkbook
withdrawal   consumption
economics   employment
wholesale   production
taxpayer   exchange
finance   savings
profit   deposit

LESSON 1

Study these list words, using the study plan on page 7.

LESSON 2

1. Write these antonyms.

deposit Money placed into a bank account	OPPOSITES	**withdrawal** Money removed from a bank account
retail The sale of goods to the general public		**wholesale** The sale of goods to those who re-sell to the public
production The creation of goods for sale and use		**consumption** The use of goods

2. Write: **economics** _____ 'Economics' is the science dealing with the production, distribution, and consumption of goods.

3. Three list words name *people* who are involved in some aspect of economics. Find the three words and write them below.

_____   _____   _____

LESSON 3

1. Write list words with these suffixes or ending syllables.

-tion _____

_____

-ing(s) _____

_____

_____

-it _____

_____

_____

-ment _____

-er _____

_____

2. Write list words with these prefixes or beginning syllables.

pro- _____

_____

ex- _____

em- _____

con- _____

de- _____

re- _____

Two of your list words are plural in form but usually singular in usage. Write these words:

economics_____
Economics is said to be a science.

savings_____
A savings is an amount of money not spent.

3. Combine words from Group A and Group B to form compound list words.

A
check
sales
whole
tax

_____

_____

_____

_____

B
man
book
payer
sale

4. Write your list words in alphabetical order. Fill in the blanks below, starting with the left column and moving downward in each column.

_____ _____ _____ _____

_____ _____ _____ _____

_____ _____ _____ _____

_____ _____ _____ _____

Study your word list. Take a practice test after completing Lesson 3.

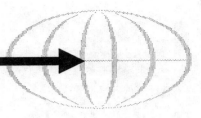

LESSON 4   *The World of Words*

1. Write all your list words three times on a separate sheet of paper.

2. Write Proverbs 13:11 (KJV).

3. Complete this saying with a list word from Unit 23 and a list word from Unit 24. (Clue: the two adjectives rhyme.)

   "Early to bed and early to rise
   Makes a man _____, _____, and wise."

   (Benjamin Franklin)

4. Write these list words. Look them up in a dictionary and write a brief definition.

   finance _____

   marketing _____

   credit _____

   profit _____

   cashier _____

5. What are these? (Use list words in your answers.)

   _____

   _____

LESSON 5

Review your word list and take your final test. Write the words in the spaces provided at the back of this book. If you have studied, God will help you.

UNIT 25

THE WORLD OF FOOD

soup	fruit
pizza	carrots
cereal	peaches
bananas	casserole
hamburger	chop suey
frankfurter	vegetable
spaghetti	cucumber
macaroni	sandwich
pastry	lettuce
taco	toast

LESSON 1

Study these list words, using the study plan on page 7.

LESSON 2

1. Write: **vegetable.** _____ Write the names of three vegetables from your word list.

   _____   _____   _____

2. Write: **fruit.** _____ Write the names of two fruits from your word list.

   _____   _____

3. Write the names of a Mexican food, a Chinese dish and two Italian foods.

   _____   _____   _____   _____

4. Two favorite breakfast foods are: _____

5. 'Casserole' is a name for both a dish and food that is cooked in it. The dish may be made of earthenware, glass, porcelain, or metal. The dish is made so the food can be both cooked and served in it. Foods cooked and served in a casserole dish are often nicknamed 'hot dishes.' Write: **casserole.**

   _____

80

LESSON 3

The food we now call a 'hamburger' was originally called a 'hamburg steak.' It is named after a city in Germany called Hamburg.

In America, the 'hamburger,' a patty of ground beef, is almost always served on a round bun. In Europe, when ordering a hamburger at a restaurant, you must often specify whether you want it on bread or served alone as a ground steak, perhaps with fried or mashed potatoes or some other side dish.

Write: **hamburger.**

_____

The All-American food we call a 'hot dog' consists of a sausage known as a 'frankfurter' served on a long roll or bun, along with ketchup, mustard, pickles, relish or other garnishments. 'Frankfurters' are named after a German city called Frankfurt. Germany is famous for a variety of sausages. A frankfurter is a sausage usually made of beef or a cooked mixture of beef, pork, chicken or turkey stuffed into a casing or formed into a sausage shape.

Write: **frankfurter.**

_____

A 'sandwich' consists of two slices of bread, with meat, cheese, jam, or some other tasty substance spread between them. It is believed to be named after John Montagu, the 4th Earl of Sandwich, an English politician who was once in charge of the British navy. His mishandling of the navy is blamed in part for the defeat of the British during the American War of Independence. The Sandwich (Hawaiian) Islands were also named after him. Write: **sandwich.** _____

Write your list words in alphabetical order. Fill in the blanks below, starting with the left column and moving downward in each column.

_____   _____   _____   _____

_____   _____   _____   _____

_____   _____   _____   _____

_____   _____   _____   _____

_____   _____   _____   _____

Study your word list. Take a practice test after completing Lesson 3.

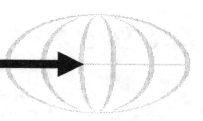

1. Write all your list words three times on a separate sheet of paper.

2. Write 1 Corinthians 10:31 (KJV).

_____

_____

_____

3. Name these foods with list words. Choose: { bananas, pizza, pastry, carrots, cucumber, or taco

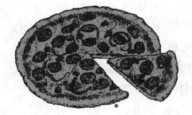      

_____   _____   _____

_____   _____   _____

4. Write a list word that sounds like 'Let us.' _____

5. Which of these is a list word? **soap** or **soup** _____

LESSON 5

Review your word list and take your final test. Write the words in the spaces provided at the back of this book. If you have studied, God will help you.

UNIT 26

THE ELEMENTS OF MATTER

iron   lead
nickel   carbon
copper   oxygen
hydrogen   mercury
potassium   platinum
aluminum   chlorine
nitrogen   calcium
sulfur*   sodium
silver   iodine
gold   zinc

LESSON 1

Study these list words, using the study plan on page 7.

* Also spelled sulphur

LESSON 2

1. Scientists now believe that all of the forms of matter in the world are made of one or a combination of some of 109 basic elements. Your word list for this unit includes 20 of the most common of them. Each of the elements has been given an abbreviation, known as its 'chemical symbol.' Study this chart of chemical symbols. Then write the element names in the blanks below.

Al Aluminum	Ca Calcium	C Carbon	Cl Chlorine	Cu Copper	Au Gold	H Hydrogen	I Iodine	Fe Iron	Pb Lead
Hg Mercury	Ni Nickel	N Nitrogen	O Oxygen	Pt Platinum	K Potassium	Ag Silver	Na Sodium	S Sulfur	Zn Zinc

Cu _____   Na _____   Hg _____   Fe _____

K _____   Ca _____   Au _____   O _____

Cl _____   I _____   Ni _____   Zn _____

Ag _____   Al _____   Pt _____   Pb _____

C _____   H _____   N _____   S _____

LESSON 3

1. Read the following information about some of the elements on your word list. Write the names of the elements.

_____ **hydrogen** – The most abundant element in the universe. Seventy percent of the universe is made of hydrogen. It is found commonly in water. It is used in the production of vegetable cooking oils.

_____ **oxygen** – The most abundant element in the earth's crust, accounting for half of it. It is an important element of the earth's atmosphere and needed by humans and animals to breath. It is used to make steel.

_____ **nitrogen** – The most abundant element (78 percent) in our air. More than 37 billion pounds are taken out of the air each year in the United States for various uses, such as fertilizer, and for keeping things very cold.

_____ **sulfur** – This element smells like rotten eggs when combined with hydrogen. Sulfur is used to produce sulfuric acid, insect killers, medicines, gunpowder, dyes, photographic materials, and cloth.

_____ **chlorine** – Chlorine, sometimes combined with oxygen, is used for bleaching paper and cloth. Laundry bleach includes chlorine. It is also used for purifying drinking water and water in swimming pools.

_____ **iodine** – Iodine is commonly found in some table salts. It is useful in our diet for the health of an organ called the thyroid gland. Iodine, combined with alcohol, also makes an ointment for cleansing cuts and scratches.

_____ **sodium** – Sodium is a kind of metal. It is a major element in salt. Sodium is used in street lamps, in the manufacture of paper, rayon, soap, cleansers, petroleum products, glass, and medicines.

_____ **iron** – The fourth most abundant element in the earth's crust. It is the cheapest metal to produce. It is also the most widely used metal because it is used in the production of steel.

_____ **copper** – Copper is one of the best metals for conducting electricity and heat. It is used for electrical wires and in cookware. The U.S. coin known as a penny has copper in it. It is also used in brass screws and jewelry.

_____ **gold** – Gold has been highly prized for its beauty and value throughout the centuries. It is used in coins and jewelry, for false teeth, and in medicine. In the Bible, gold describes the glories of heaven and righteousness.

2. Write your list words in alphabetical order. Fill in the blanks below, starting with the left column and moving downward in each column.

_____   _____   _____   _____

_____   _____   _____   _____

_____   _____   _____   _____

_____   _____   _____   _____

_____   _____   _____   _____

> *Study your word list. Take a practice test after completing Lesson 3.*

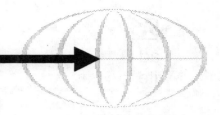

1. Write all your list words three times on a separate sheet of paper.

2. Write Psalm 19:10 (KJV), which tells something about God's commandments.

_____

_____

_____

_____

_____ **aluminum** - The most abundant metal on earth. It is easily molded and lightweight. It is used in trim for cars and buildings and for aircraft parts and cooking utensils. It is also used in drain cleaners and anti-perspirant deodorants.

_____ **silver** - Silver is a relatively soft, bright metal that is the best metal for conducting heat and electricity. However, its high cost prohibits its use for electrical wires. It is used in jewelry, coins, fine dishes, and photo film.

_____ **nickel** - Nickel is a bright, silver-white metal. It is hard and takes a good polish. Often combined with other metals, it adds strength, can be drawn out into wire, and is resistant to heat and corrosion.

_____ **potassium** - Potassium is another silver-white metal. It is soft, and it is an important mineral for the human diet. It has little commercial value in its pure form but is useful when combined with other elements.

_____ **lead** - Lead is a very heavy metal and one of the oldest metals used by man. It is soft and is a poor electricity conductor. It is a shield against radiation and is used in batteries and fine glass. It is poisonous in combined forms.

_____ **carbon** - An abundant non-metal element found in all living matter. All life on earth depends on interactions between carbon, oxygen, and hydrogen. It is a fuel and is found in coal and oil. Crystal carbon forms diamonds.

_____ **mercury** - Sometimes called 'quicksilver.' It is a silvery, liquid metal used in thermometers and barometers. When electricity is passed through it, it vaporizes, giving off a greenish-blue light often seen in street lamps.

_____ **platinum** - A grayish-white metal, it is easily molded and drawn out. It is valued for its resistance to corrosion and its beauty. It is used in jewelry, electrical wires, laboratory utensils, weights, and foils.

_____ **calcium** - Calcium is a silvery-white metal that is very important to the human diet. It helps build strong bones and teeth, helps to regulate the heartbeat, and helps in blood clotting.

_____ **zinc** - Zinc is a bluish-white metal. It is useful as a coating for iron to prevent rusting. Combined with oxygen, it is used in a soothing ointment that heals skin irritations such as babies' diaper rash. Also used in batteries.

LESSON 5

Review your word list and take your final test. Write the words in the spaces provided at the back of this book. Ask God in prayer for help with your test.

U_{NIT} 27

THE WORLD OF ANIMALS

lion	tiger
koala	llama
giraffe	antelope
buffalo	opossum
rhinoceros	chimpanzee
dromedary	hippopotamus
kangaroo	elephant
cheetah	reindeer
gorilla	raccoon
wolf	moose

LESSON 1

Study these list words, using the study plan on page 7.

LESSON 2

1. Write the names of these three big members of the cat family.

   lion _____

   tiger _____

   cheetah _____

2. Write the names of these two members of the ape family.

   chimpanzee _____

   gorilla _____

3. Write the names of these two animals related to the camel.

   dromedary _____

   llama _____

4. Write the names of these three African giants.

   elephant _____

   rhinoceros _____

   hippopotamus _____

5. Write the names of these two deer-like animals.

   reindeer _____

   antelope _____

6. Write the names of these nocturnal (night-active) animals.

   opossum _____

   raccoon _____

LESSON 3

1. Name these animals with list words.

_____

_____

_____

_____

_____

_____

_____

_____

_____

2. Write your list words in alphabetical order. Fill in the blanks below, starting with the left column and moving downward in each column.

_____	_____	_____	_____
_____	_____	_____	_____
_____	_____	_____	_____
_____	_____	_____	_____

Study your word list. Take a practice test after completing Lesson 3.

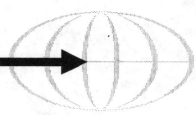

1. Write all your list words three times on a separate sheet of paper.

2. Write Genesis 1:24 (KJV).

_____

_____

_____

3. Name these animals with list words.

_____   _____   _____

_____   _____   _____

_____

LESSON 5

Review your word list and take your final test. Write the words in the spaces provided at the back of this book. Ask God in prayer for help with your test.

UNIT 28

THE WORLD OF PETS

LESSON 1

Study these list words, using the study plan on page 7.

manx	collie
angora	poodle
siamese	canary
parakeet	guinea pig
dachshund	salamander
shepherd	hamster
retriever	goldfish
spaniel	guppy
beagle	rabbit
terrier	turtle

LESSON 2

1. Write the names of these three breeds of cats.

   manx _____

   angora _____

   siamese _____

2. Write the names of these two kinds of pet birds.

   parakeet _____

   canary _____

3. Write the names of these two pet reptiles.

   salamander _____

   turtle _____

4. Write the names of these three furry pets.

   rabbit _____

   hamster _____

   guinea pig _____

5. Write the names of these breeds of dogs.

   collie _____

   terrier _____

   poodle _____

   beagle _____

   spaniel _____

   retriever _____

   shepherd _____

   dachshund _____

LESSON 3

1. Name these pets with list words.

Hamster

Guinea Pig

Rabbit

_____

_____

_____

Parakeet

Canary

Turtle

_____

_____

_____

Salamander

Goldfish

Siamese Cat

_____

_____

_____

2. Write your list words in alphabetical order. Fill in the blanks below, starting with the left column and moving downward in each column.

_____   _____   _____   _____

_____   _____   _____   _____

_____   _____   _____   _____

_____   _____   _____   _____

_____   _____   _____   _____

Study your word list. Take a practice test after completing Lesson 3.

90

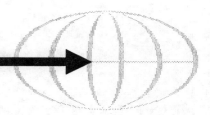

1. Write all your list words three times on a separate sheet of paper.

2. Write Isaiah 40:1 (KJV).

3. Write the names of these four kinds of dogs.

Beagle

Terrier

Shepherd

Spaniel

4. Write the names of two pets from your word list that you would keep in an aquarium.

5. Which of the animals on your word list would you prefer to have for pets?

6. Write all list words that have double consonants.

7. Write all list words that have double vowels.

LESSON 5

Review your word list and take your final test. Write the words in the spaces provided at the back of this book. Ask God in prayer for help with your test.

UNIT 29

TERMS RELATED TO CHURCH

LESSON 1

Study these list words, using the study plan on page 7.

choir	elders
hymns	pastors
psalms	deacons
sermon	teachers
preaching	communion
fellowship	congregation
sanctuary	ministry
worship	offering
praise	prayer
organ	liturgy

LESSON 2

1. Write the names of four kinds of leaders God has given to His Church to guide it and build up the faith of His people. Use list words.

_____

_____

_____

_____

2. God has given many gifts to His people. Which list word describes how we thankfully return some of God's gifts to Him for use in His service?

_____

3. 'Worship' is giving love, reverence, esteem, and devotion to God. Write: **worship.**_____
Write some list words which name ways we may worship God during a church service.

_____

_____

_____

_____

_____

_____

4. Write a list word that means:
A group of people who gather regularly for worship.

_____

LESSON 3

1. Study or review these spelling rules about adding suffixes to base words.

> **1** When a word ends with a consonant preceded by a vowel, the last consonant is doubled before adding a suffix that begins with a vowel.
>
> **2** When a word ends with two consonants, the last consonant is NOT doubled before adding a suffix that begins with a vowel.
>
> **3** When a word ends with silent 'e,' the 'e' is dropped before adding a suffix beginning with a vowel. Keep final 'e' when adding a suffix beginning with a consonant.

2. Using the rules above, add the suffixes to the base words below.

worship + er _____

preach + ing _____

pray + er _____

praise + ing _____

commune + ion _____

teach + ers _____

fellowship + ing _____

preach + er _____

teach + ing _____

worship + ing _____

pray + ing _____

congregate + ion _____

I love Thy Church, O God!
Her walls before Thee stand,
Dear as the apple of Thine eye,
And graven on Thy hand.
□ Timothy Dwight

3. Write: **offering.** _____

Does the spelling of this word follow Rule 1 above or is it an exception to the rule?

Check One:
- [ ] **Follows the rule**
- [ ] **Exception to the rule**

4. Write your list words in alphabetical order. Fill in the blanks below, starting with the left column and moving downward in each column.

_____ _____ _____ _____

_____ _____ _____ _____

_____ _____ _____ _____

_____ _____ _____ _____

Study your word list. Take a practice test after completing Lesson 3.

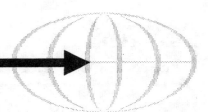

1. Write all your list words three times on a separate sheet of paper.

2. Write Ephesians 3:21 (KJV).

---

3. Read these verses from the Bible (KJV). Write the list words they contain.

John 4:24 _____

Ephesians 5:19 _____

_____

Psalm 150:1 _____

_____

Psalm 1:5 _____

2 Corinthians 6:14 _____

_____

1 Corinthians 15:14 _____

Ephesians 4:11-12 _____

_____

_____

1 Timothy 3:12 _____

1 Timothy 5:17 _____

Psalm 96:8 _____

Psalm 5:3 _____

Learn or review the following phonics rules about the consonant digraph 'ch':

'Ch' has three sounds in English words:
1. *The sound of 'tsh' as in 'church,'*
2. *The sound of 'k' as in 'kite,'*
3. *The sound of 'sh' as in 'wish.'*

Write: **choir** _____

☐ Which sound does 'ch' have in this word? (1, 2, or 3)

Write: **teachers** _____

☐ Which sound does 'ch' have in this word? (1, 2, or 3)

Write: **preaching** _____

☐ Which sound does 'ch' have in this word? (1, 2, or 3)

4. Write: **liturgy** _____

MEANING: A series of ceremonies or procedures used for public worship. A prescribed formula for a religious service or ceremony.

LESSON 5

Review your word list and take your final test. Write the words in the spaces provided at the back of this book. Ask God in prayer for help with your test.

UNIT 30

THE WORLD OF THE ELDERLY

aged   elderly
senior   pension
wisdom   leadership
volunteer   experience
grandmother   grandparents
grandfather   grandchildren
anniversary   retirement
gardening   painting
traveling   knitting
quilting   fishing

LESSON 1

Study these list words, using the study plan on page 7.

LESSON 2

1. When people reach old age, they are often referred to using terms such as those below. Write the list words you find in these terms.

   "senior citizens" _____

   "the aged" _____

   "the elderly" _____

2. Elderly people, especially those who have lived godly lives, have much to offer to younger people. Write three list words which name qualities often found in the aged.

   _____

   _____

   _____

3. Many old people like to continue working well into their senior years if health permits. Others retire from work and enjoy leisure activities. The last three words in each column of your word list name some things the elderly enjoy. Write these words.

   _____

   _____

   _____

   _____

   _____

   _____

4. The oldest man ever was Methuselah. How many years did he live? (See Genesis 5:27.) _____

95

LESSON 3

1. Fill in the blanks with list words.

    a. Your mom's or dad's mother is your_____

    b. Your mom's or dad's father is your_____

    c. Your children's children will be your_____

    d. Your grandma and grandpa are your_____

2. Circle the list words you find in this paragraph. Write the words in the box.

    Volunteer service is a term often associated with the elderly. Many older people, with extra time on their hands, spend part of their retirement years offering their services for free in various community or church programs. Senior citizens, whose pension may not provide all the income they need, often are the recipients of service by others. Some give time to helping the aged with their needs out of gratitude for the experience, wisdom and leadership they have given to younger generations over the years.

3. Use list words to label the activities shown in these pictures.

    _____   _____   _____

4. Write your list words in alphabetical order. Fill in the blanks below, starting with the left column and moving downward in each column.

_____   _____   _____

_____   _____   _____

_____   _____   _____

_____   _____   _____

Study your word list. Take a practice test after completing Lesson 3.

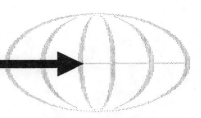

1. Write all your list words three times on a separate sheet of paper.

2. Read Psalm 90 (KJV). Write verse 12 below.

_____

_____

_____

3. Add these suffixes to these base words to form list words.

fish + ing _____

travel + ing _____

knit + ing _____

garden + ing _____

quilt + ing _____

leader + ship _____

retire + ment _____

age + ed _____

Which of the list words you have written above are exceptions to the spelling rules on page 93?

_____

_____

Happy 50th!

These people have been married for 50 years. They are celebrating their Golden Wedding _____ .

(Fill in the blank with a list word.)

4. The word 'aged' can be a verb (past tense) or an adjective (usually pronounced 'ajed'). In recent years, it is also being used as a noun. Example: 'a home for the aged.' When used as a noun, it is usually pronounced 'ajed.'

5. Write: **pension** _____

MEANING: An amount of money paid regularly to a retired person, usually based on the number of years he or she has worked or paid into the pension investment program.

LESSON 5

Review your word list and take your final test. Write the words in the spaces provided at the back of this book. Ask God in prayer for help with your test.

UNIT 31

THE WORLD OF ARTS AND ENTERTAINMENT

radio   opera
ballet   author
concert   theater
orchestra cassette
symphony   compact disc
performance entertainment
television playwright
sculpture   comedy
artistic   movies
video   drama

LESSON 1

Study these list words, using the study plan on page 7.

LESSON 2

1. Write: **artistic.** _____ This word is an adjective meaning: having the quality of an **artist**; having great skill or ability in the arts (painting, music, sculpture, dancing, writing, etc.). Write the list words below left and their adjective forms. Notice the spelling (and accent) changes carefully.

<table>
<tr><td></td><td></td><td></td><td>Changes</td></tr>
<tr><td>cómedy _____</td><td>→</td><td>comédic _____</td><td>(- y)</td></tr>
<tr><td>dráma _____</td><td>→</td><td>dramátic _____</td><td>(+t)</td></tr>
<tr><td>sýmphony _____</td><td>→</td><td>symphónic _____</td><td>(- y)</td></tr>
<tr><td>ópera _____</td><td>→</td><td>operátic _____</td><td>(+t)</td></tr>
<tr><td>théater _____</td><td>→</td><td>theátric* _____</td><td>(- e)</td></tr>
</table>

* A more common adjective form is: 'theatrical.'

2. Write these homonyms:

right _____

write _____

wright _____

rite _____

Which of the words at the left properly completes this compound list word? **play**_____

A 'wright' is a worker or maker. Thus a 'millwright' is a worker in a mill. A 'shipwright' is a maker of ships. A 'playwright' is a 'maker' of a play. Just because a playwright 'writes' plays, do not confuse the spelling of the second syllable. 'Wright' is right, 'write' is wrong. Right?

LESSON 3

1. Identify these sound- and image-recording devices with list words.

 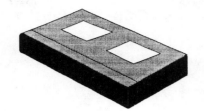 

audio _____   _____   _____

2. Write these words and the related words naming people involved in the world of arts and entertainment. Carefully note word endings in column two.

books _____	author _____
entertainment _____	entertainer _____
performance _____	performer _____
sculpture _____	sculptor _____
ballet _____	ballerina _____
artistic _____	artist _____
orchestra _____	orchestrator* _____
drama _____	dramatist _____
comedy _____	comedian** _____
theater _____	playwright _____

* May also be spelled 'orchestrater.'   **This is the masculine spelling. Feminine is 'comedienne.'

4. Write your list words in alphabetical order. Fill in the blanks below, starting with the left column and moving downward in each column.

_____ _____ _____ _____

_____ _____ _____ _____

_____ _____ _____ _____

_____ _____ _____ _____

_____ _____ _____ _____

Study your word list. Take a practice test after completing Lesson 3.

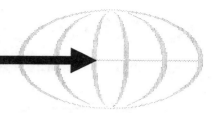

1. Write all your list words three times on a separate sheet of paper.

2. Write Philippians 4:8 (KJV).

3. Write a sentence using these list words: | **symphony - orchestra - concert**

4. Write a sentence using these list words: | **theater - drama - comedy**

5. Write a sentence using these list words: | **opera - radio - performance**

6. Write a sentence using these list words: | **television - movies - entertainment**

7. Write a sentence using these list words: | **cassette - video**

LESSON 5

Review your word list and take your final test. Write the words in the spaces provided at the back of this book. Ask God in prayer for help with your test.

UNIT 32

THE WORLD OF TRAVEL AND TRANSPORTATION

truck   barge
airline   railroad
airport   gasoline
aircraft   helicopter
reservation automobile
transportation snowmobile
passenger   motorcycle
commuter   riverboat
cruise   vehicle
coach   depot

LESSON 1

Study these list words, using the study plan on page 7.

LESSON 2

1. Write two compound list words that include the word 'mobile."

_____

_____

2. Write two list words ending with the suffix '-ation.'

_____

_____

3. From the list at the right, select two related words to write in each box.

	airport
_____	cruise
_____	depot
_____	aircraft
_____	railroad
_____	riverboat

4. Write list words that name vehicles used for transportation on land.

_____

_____

_____

_____

5. Write list words that name vehicles used for transportation on water.

_____

_____

6. Write list words that name vehicles used for transportation in the air.

_____

_____

101

LESSON 3

1. Name these pictures with list words. Choose: railroad, helicopter, motorcycle, coach, riverboat, snowmobile, truck, automobile, or aircraft.

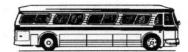

2. Write your list words in alphabetical order. Fill in the blanks below, starting with the left column and moving downward in each column.

_____   _____   _____   _____

_____   _____   _____   _____

_____   _____   _____   _____

_____   _____   _____   _____

_____   _____   _____   _____

Study your word list. Take a practice test after completing Lesson 3.

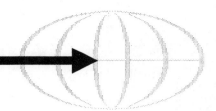

1. Write all your list words three times on a separate sheet of paper.

2. Write Psalm 107:23-24 (KJV).

_____

_____

_____

_____

_____

3. Write: **depot.**_____ Find this word in a dictionary. Learn the meaning, and learn how to pronounce the word. Which letter is silent? _____

4. Write these list words. Then write the letter of the correct definition in the box.

☐ **commuter**	A. A device used for the transportation of goods, passengers, or equipment.
☐ **barge**	B. Someone who travels regularly between two places, such as a home outside a city to a place of work in a city.
☐ **reservation**	C. Any means, act, or process of carrying objects or any means of travel.
☐ **cruise**	D. (Verb) To travel about, usually for pleasure; (Noun) A journey from port to port, usually on a ship.
☐ **vehicle**	E. Anyone who rides in a vehicle.
☐ **passenger**	F. An enclosed carriage; a bus; a railroad passenger car
☐ **transportation**	G. A flat-bottomed boat that is towed through a river or canal and is used for transporting freight.
☐ **coach**	H. An arrangement by which travel tickets or lodging may be secured ahead of time

LESSON 5

Review your word list and take your final test. Write the words in the spaces provided at the back of this book. Ask God in prayer for help with your test.

UNIT 33

THE WORLD OF BOOKS

atlas   novel
journal   textbook
bindery   workbook
bookstore   handbook
dictionary   paperback
encyclopedia   commentary
thesaurus   publisher
almanac   pamphlet
lexicon   directory
diary   fiction

LESSON 1

Study these list words, using the study plan on page 7.

LESSON 2

1. Complete these list words and learn their meanings.

_____ **ary** = A book containing definitions of words and information about words.

_____ **ary** = A book of comments or opinions on a subject, such as a Bible passage.

_____ **ary** = A book for keeping a daily record of personal events, interests, ideas, etc.

_____ **ory** = A book containing lists of information, such as names or telephone numbers.

_____ **ery** = A place of business that binds the pages and covers of books together.

2. Write a list word that means: 'a book of synonyms.' _____
   Write these synonyms that can be found in a thesaurus.

dictionary _____   **diary** _____

lexicon _____   **journal** _____

novel _____   **textbook** _____

fiction _____   **handbook** _____

3. Write two list words that could describe the schoolbook you are now using.

_____   _____

LESSON 3

1. Fill in the blanks in the paragraphs below with list words.

HOW BOOKS ARE MADE AND SOLD

A book begins when a writer has an idea, story, or other information and puts his thoughts on paper. This paper is called a manuscript. The author next finds a business that is willing to get the book printed, bound, distributed, and sold. This business that oversees the publication of books is called a _____.

A factory that binds book pages together and puts covers on them is called a _____. Books are bound either with hard covers (usually made of a stiff material covered by cloth) or with soft covers. A book with a soft cover is sometimes called a _____ . A very short booklet with a paper cover or no cover and sometimes no binding is called a _____. When books are manufactured, they begin at the printing plant. They then go to a bindery, which may be part of the printing plant or a separate establishment. They are then taken by a distributor to a _____ where they are sold to the public.

2. Write: **encyclopedia.** _____

An encyclopedia is a book or set of books that contains a great volume of information about all of the branches of human knowledge. This information is usually written in separate articles on various subjects, arranged alphabetically.

3. Write: **almanac.** _____

An almanac is a book or magazine that is published every year and contains calendars, weather forecasts, information about the movement of stars, tables of statistics, and sometimes articles expressing down-to-earth wisdom.

4. Write your list words in alphabetical order. Fill in the blanks below, starting with the left column and moving downward in each column.

_____ _____ _____ _____

_____ _____ _____ _____

_____ _____ _____ _____

_____ _____ _____ _____

_____ _____ _____ _____

Study your word list. Take a practice test after completing Lesson 3.

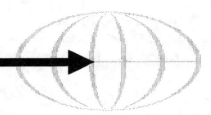

1. Write all your list words three times on a separate sheet of paper.

2. Write John 21:25 (KJV).

_____

_____

_____

_____

_____

3. Which list word names a book that contains these? ➝

_____

4. When you visit a library, you may notice that books are generally classified as fiction, non-fiction, or reference books.

Write: **fiction.** _____

Fiction books are books that contain stories created in the imagination of the writer. Fiction works include: short stories, plays, and _____.

Non-fiction books are all those that are based on fact, rather than imagination. These books include reference books, which are books intended to be consulted from time to time for specific information rather than to be read from cover to cover. Reference books are usually not intended to be taken from a library. These kinds of books include: *(write these plural words)*

encyclopedias _____   **atlases** _____

dictionaries _____   **almanacs** _____

thesauruses _____   **lexicons** _____

directories _____

LESSON 5

Review your word list and take your final test. Write the words in the spaces provided at the back of this book. Ask God in prayer for help with your test.

Review:

The World of Words

This double unit includes words
from each of the 33 previous units
in this book. Review all of these words.
Be prepared to be tested on 20 of them to be
selected by your teacher. Write the words shown.

Unit 1: Countries of the Western Hemisphere

United States _____

Canada _____

Mexico _____

Brazil _____

Argentina _____

Unit 2: Countries of Western Europe

England _____

France _____

Germany _____

Italy _____

Sweden _____

Unit 3: Countries of Eastern Europe

Russia _____

Hungary _____

Greece _____

Poland _____

Bulgaria _____

Unit 4: Countries of Asia

China _____

Japan _____

India _____

Korea _____

Taiwan _____

Unit 5: Countries of Africa

South Africa _____

Nigeria _____

Ethiopia _____

Kenya _____

Zimbabwe _____

Unit 6: Countries of the Middle East

Israel _____

Egypt _____

Iraq _____

Syria _____

Libya _____

Unit 7: Eastern United States

Michigan _____

Connecticut _____

Virginia _____

New York _____

Mississippi _____

Unit 8: Western United States

Montana _____

California _____

Colorado _____

Texas _____

Hawaii _____

Unit 9: The World of Astronomy

astronomy _____

galaxy _____

meteor _____

planetarium _____

Earth _____

Unit 10: The World of Flowers

marigold _____

dandelion _____

petunia _____

daffodil _____

violet _____

Unit 11: The World of Music

melody _____

harmony _____

piano _____

guitar _____

clarinet _____

Unit 12: The World of Business

corporation _____

account _____

customer _____

capital _____

invoice _____

Unit 13: The World of Geography

continent _____

geography _____

peninsula _____

equator _____

plateau _____

Unit 14: The World of Birds

eagle _____

pheasant _____

turkey _____

flamingo _____

cardinal _____

Unit 15: The World of Sports

baseball _____

archery _____

basketball _____

gymnastics _____

hockey _____

Unit 16: Kinds of Buildings

tabernacle _____

courthouse _____

restaurant _____

dormitory _____

hospital _____

Unit 17: The World of Anatomy

abdomen _____

muscle _____

stomach _____

lungs _____

intestine _____

Unit 18: Forms and Offices of Government

democracy _____

republic _____

legislature _____

presidency _____

kingdom _____

Unit 19: Titles for Civil Officers

mayor _____

sheriff _____

governor _____

councilman _____

treasurer _____

Unit 20: Scientific and Technical Instruments

microscope _____

thermometer _____

speedometer _____

generator _____

camera _____

Unit 21: The World of Law

defendant _____

felony _____

justice _____

homicide _____

lawyer _____

Unit 22: The World of Trees

maple _____

aspen _____

hickory _____

sycamore _____

spruce _____

Unit 23: The World of Health

medicine _____

exercise _____

nutrition _____

disease _____

surgery _____

Unit 24: The World of Economics

retail _____

economics _____

finance _____

cashier _____

employment _____

Unit 25: The World of Food

hamburger _____

casserole _____

vegetable _____

macaroni _____

sandwich _____

Unit 26: The Elements of Matter

mercury _____

calcium _____

oxygen _____

hydrogen _____

aluminum _____

Unit 27: The World of Animals

raccoon _____

gorilla _____

moose _____

buffalo _____

llama _____

Unit 28: The World of Pets

parakeet _____

hamster _____

dachshund _____

spaniel _____

salamander _____

Unit 29: Terms Related to Church

worship _____

praise _____

prayer _____

ministry _____

communion _____

Unit 30: The World of the Elderly

elderly _____

pension _____

retirement _____

wisdom _____

grandparents _____

Unit 31: The World of Arts and Entertainment

concert _____

symphony _____

ballet _____

television _____

entertainment _____

Unit 32: World of Travel and Transportation

aircraft _____

passenger _____

gasoline _____

cruise _____

depot _____

Unit 33: The World of Books

almanac _____

encyclopedia _____

dictionary _____

pamphlet _____

publisher _____

The World of Words ...

... Bringing into captivity every thought to the obedience of Christ. (2 Corinthians 10:5b)

UNIT 36

THE WORLD OF VACATION

cabin	leisure
cookout	boating
camping	outdoors
swimming	barbecue
relaxation	mountains
sunbathing	backyard
recreation	bicycling
vacation	summer
projects	reading
beach	tourist

LESSON 1

Study these list words, using the study plan on page 7.

LESSON 2

1. Write: **tourist.** _____

A tourist is a person who travels for enjoyment. If you could travel to a foreign country for your summer vacation, which five countries among those listed in Units 1-6 would you choose? If you could travel in the United States, which five states of those listed in Units 7 and 8 would you choose?

Countries	**States**
_____	_____
_____	_____
_____	_____
_____	_____
_____	_____

2. Write: **summer projects.**

_____ _____

Summer projects are constructive activities you could do during your summer vacation from school, such as building a treehouse. Name three summer projects that would be of interest to you. (Use your own words.)

1. _____
2. _____
3. _____

3. A highlight of the summer for many children is V.B.S. Perhaps you could attend a session at a church nearby. Write: **Vacation Bible School.**

LESSON 3

1. Complete these list words.

re __ __ __ ation
re __ __ __ ation
__ __ __ ation

__ __ __ __ __ ing
__ __ __ __ __ ing
__ __ __ __ __ ing
__ __ __ __ __ __ ing
__ __ __ __ __ __ ing
__ __ __ __ __ __ __ ing

out __ __ __ __ __
__ __ __ __ out

__ __ __ __ ur __
__ __ ur __ __ __

2. Write two list words in which 'ea' spells the sound of long 'e.'

_____   _____

Write a list word in which 'ei' spells the sound of long 'e.'

_____

3. Write five sentences using these list words.

cabin mountains reading	
sunbathing swimming beach	
barbecue backyard cookout	
recreation relaxation leisure	
vacation summer projects	

4. Write your list words in alphabetical order. Fill in the blanks below, starting with the left column and moving downward in each column.

_____   _____   _____   _____

_____   _____   _____   _____

_____   _____   _____   _____

_____   _____   _____   _____

_____   _____   _____   _____

Study your word list. Take a practice test after completing Lesson 3.

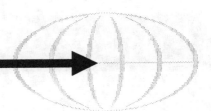
1. Write all your list words three times on a separate sheet of paper.

2. Write Mark 6:31-32 (KJV).

_____

_____

_____

_____

_____

3. Label the pictures with list words. Use: { tourists, cabin, mountains, sunbathing, beach, boating, camping, relaxation, leisure, cookout, barbecue

_____　　_____　　_____　　_____

_____　　_____　　　　　　_____

or　　　　*or*　　　　　　　　*on the*

_____　　_____　　　　　　_____

LESSON 5

Review your word list and take your final test. Write the words in the spaces provided at the back of this book. Ask God in prayer for help with your test.

UNIT 1 TEST

_____

_____

_____

_____

_____

_____

_____

_____

_____

_____

_____

_____

_____

_____

_____

_____

UNIT 2 TEST

UNIT 3 TEST

UNIT 4 TEST

_____
_____
_____
_____
_____
_____
_____
_____
_____
_____
_____
_____
_____
_____
_____
_____

UNIT 5 TEST

_____
_____
_____
_____
_____
_____
_____
_____
_____
_____
_____
_____
_____
_____
_____
_____

UNIT 6 TEST

_____
_____
_____
_____
_____
_____
_____
_____
_____
_____
_____
_____
_____
_____
_____
_____

UNIT 7 TEST

UNIT 8 TEST

UNIT 9 TEST

UNIT 10 TEST

UNIT 11 TEST

UNIT 12 TEST

UNIT 13 TEST

UNIT 14 TEST

UNIT 15 TEST

UNIT 16 TEST

UNIT 17 TEST

UNIT 18 TEST

UNIT 19 TEST

UNIT 20 TEST

UNIT 21 TEST

UNIT 22 TEST

UNIT 23 TEST

UNIT 24 TEST

UNIT 25 TEST

_____

_____

_____

_____

_____

_____

_____

_____

_____

_____

_____

_____

_____

_____

_____

_____

UNIT 26 TEST

_____

_____

_____

_____

_____

_____

_____

_____

_____

_____

_____

_____

_____

_____

_____

_____

UNIT 27 TEST

_____

_____

_____

_____

_____

_____

_____

_____

_____

_____

_____

_____

_____

_____

_____

_____

UNIT 28 TEST

UNIT 29 TEST

UNIT 30 TEST

UNIT 31 TEST

UNIT 32 TEST

UNIT 33 TEST

UNIT 34 TEST ## UNIT 35 TEST ## UNIT 36 TEST

_____

_____

_____

_____

_____

_____

_____

_____

_____

_____

_____

_____

_____

_____

_____

_____

_____

_____

_____

_____

_____

_____

_____

_____

_____

_____

_____

_____

_____

_____

_____

_____

Western Hemisphere

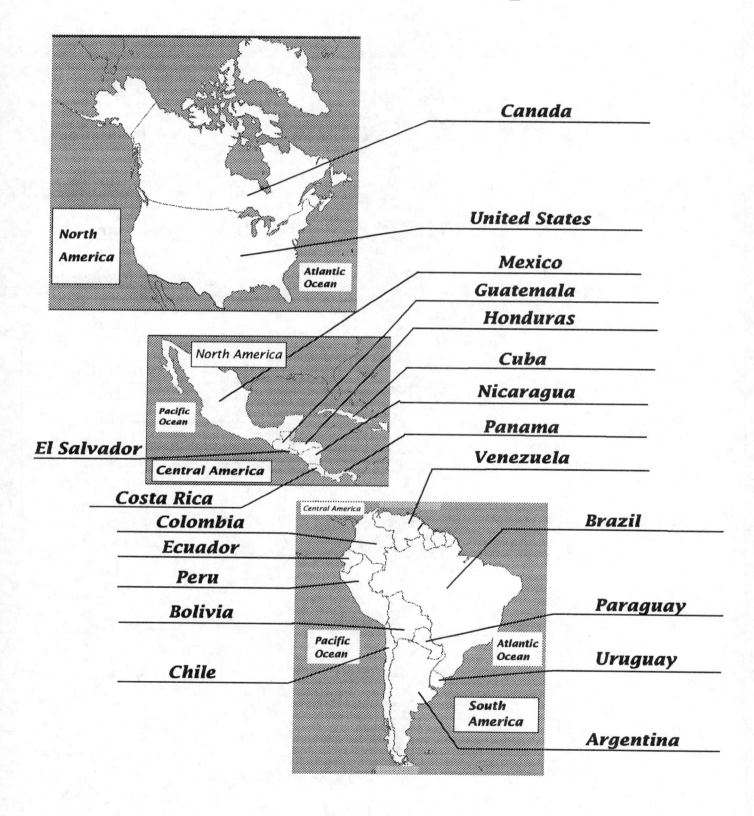

Canada

United States

Mexico

Guatemala

Honduras

Cuba

Nicaragua

Panama

Venezuela

El Salvador

Costa Rica

Colombia

Ecuador

Peru

Bolivia

Chile

Brazil

Paraguay

Uruguay

Argentina

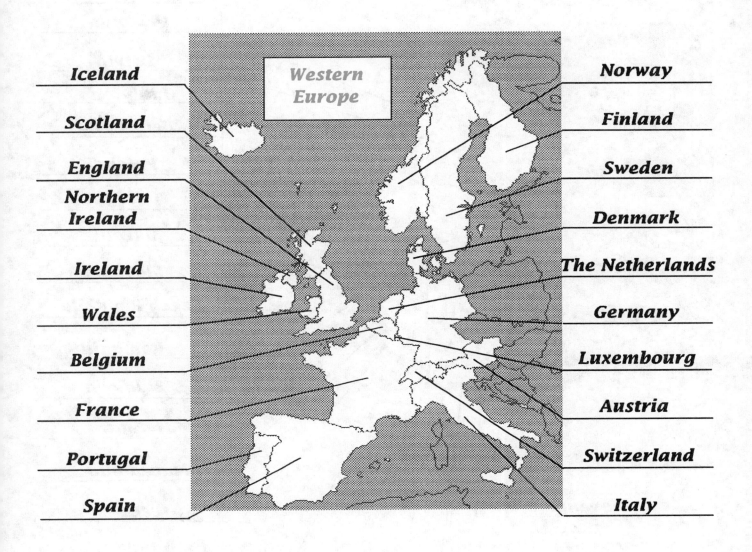

Iceland
Scotland
England
Northern Ireland
Ireland
Wales
Belgium
France
Portugal
Spain

Western Europe

Norway
Finland
Sweden
Denmark
The Netherlands
Germany
Luxembourg
Austria
Switzerland
Italy

Western Europe

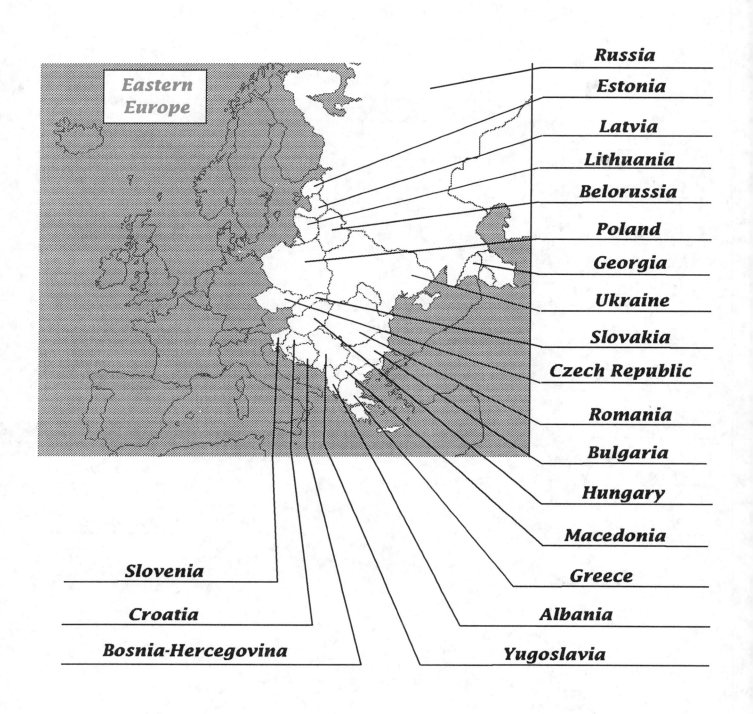

Eastern Europe

Russia
Estonia
Latvia
Lithuania
Belorussia
Poland
Georgia
Ukraine
Slovakia
Czech Republic
Romania
Bulgaria
Hungary
Macedonia
Greece
Albania
Yugoslavia
Slovenia
Croatia
Bosnia-Hercegovina

Eastern Europe

128

Asia

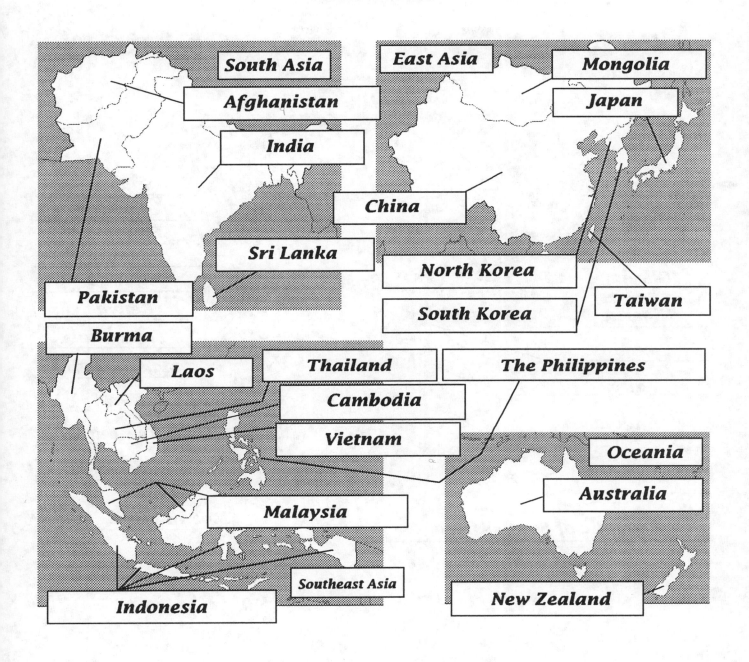

South Asia / East Asia / Mongolia / Afghanistan / India / Japan / China / North Korea / South Korea / Taiwan / Sri Lanka / Pakistan / Burma / Laos / Thailand / The Philippines / Cambodia / Vietnam / Oceania / Australia / Malaysia / Southeast Asia / Indonesia / New Zealand

South Asia

East Asia

Southeast Asia

Oceania

West, Central, and Southern

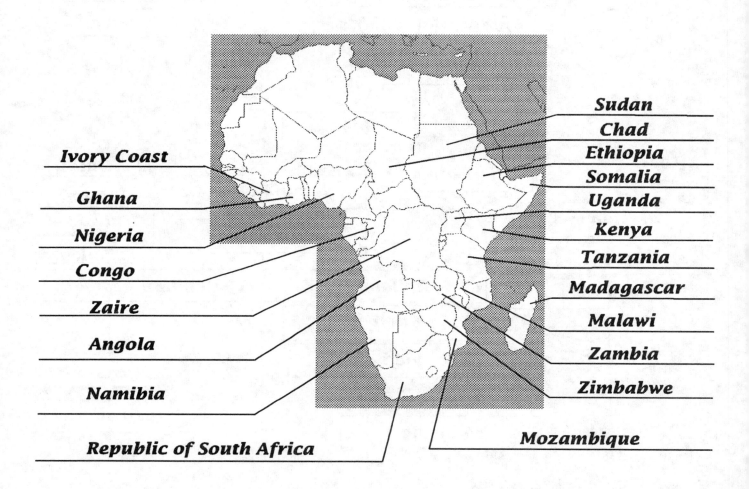

Ivory Coast

Ghana

Nigeria

Congo

Zaire

Angola

Namibia

Republic of South Africa

Sudan

Chad

Ethiopia

Somalia

Uganda

Kenya

Tanzania

Madagascar

Malawi

Zambia

Zimbabwe

Mozambique

Africa

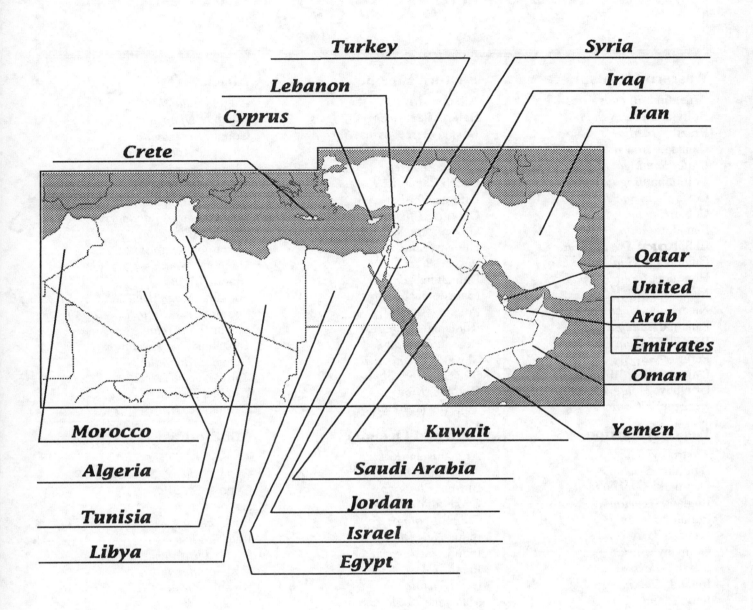

Turkey
Syria
Lebanon
Iraq
Cyprus
Iran
Crete
Qatar
United
Arab
Emirates
Oman
Morocco
Kuwait
Yemen
Algeria
Saudi Arabia
Tunisia
Jordan
Libya
Israel
Egypt

North Africa and The Middle East

COUNTRIES OF THE WORLD AND THEIR CAPITALS

Western Hemisphere

Argentina: *Buenos Aires*
Bolivia: *La Paz / Sucre*
Brazil: *Brasilia*
Canada: *Ottawa*
Chile: *Santiago*
Columbia: *Bogota*
Costa Rica: *San Jose*
Cuba: *Havana*
Ecuador: *Quito*
El Salvador: *San Salvador*
Guatemala: *Guatemala City*
Honduras: *Tegucigalpa*
Mexico: *Mexico City*
Nicaragua: *Managua*
Panama: *Panama City*
Paraguay: *Asuncion*
Peru: *Lima*
United States: *Washington*
Uruguay: *Montevideo*
Venezuela: *Caracas*

Western Europe

Austria: *Vienna*
Belgium: *Brussels*
Denmark: *Copenhagen*
England: *London*
Finland: *Helsinki*
France: *Paris*
Germany: *Berlin*
Iceland: *Reykjavik*
Ireland: *Dublin*
Italy: *Rome*
Luxembourg: *Luxembourg*
Northern Ireland: *Belfast*
Norway: *Oslo*
Portugal: *Lisbon*
Scotland: *Edinburgh*
Spain: *Madrid*
Sweden: *Stockholm*
Switzerland: *Bern*
The Netherlands: *Amsterdam / The Hague*
Wales: *Cardiff (principal city)*

Eastern Europe

Albania: *Tiranë*
Belorussia: *Minsk*
Bosnia-Hercegovina: *Sarajevo*
Bulgaria: *Sofia*
Croatia: *Zagreb*
Czech Republic: *Prague*
Estonia: *Tallinn*
Georgia: *Tiflis*
Greece: *Athens*
Hungary: *Budapest*
Latvia: *Riga*
Lithuania: *Vilnius*
Macedonia: *Skopje*
Poland: *Warsaw*
Romania: *Bucharest*
Russia: *Moscow*
Slovakia: *Bratislava*
Slovenia: *Ljubljana*
Ukraine: *Kiev*
Yugoslavia: *Belgrade*

Asia and Oceania

Afghanistan: *Kabul*
Australia: *Canberra*
Burma: *Rangoon*
Cambodia: *Phnom Penh*
China: *Beijing*
India: *New Delhi*
Indonesia: *Jakarta*
Japan: *Tokyo*
Laos: *Vientiane*
Malaysia: *Kuala Lumpur*
Mongolia: *Ulan Bator*
New Zealand: *Wellington*
North Korea: *Pyongyang*
Pakistan: *Islamabad*
South Korea: *Seoul*
Sri Lanka: *Colombo*
Taiwan: *Taipei*
Thailand: *Bangkok*
The Philippines: *Manila*
Vietnam: *Hanoi*

Africa

Angola: *Luanda*
Chad: *N'Djamena*
Congo: *Brazzaville*
Ethiopia: *Addis Ababa*
Ghana: *Accra*
Ivory Coast: *Abidjan*
Kenya: *Nairobi*
Madagascar: *Antananarivo*
Malawi: *Lilongwe*
Mozambique: *Maputo*
Namibia: *Windhoek*
Nigeria: *Abuja*
Somalia: *Mogadishu*
South Africa: *Pretoria / Cape Town*
Sudan: *Khartoum*
Tanzania: *Dar es Salaam*
Uganda: *Kampala*
Zaire: *Kinshasa*
Zambia: *Lusaka*
Zimbabwe: *Harare*

Middle East

Algeria: *Algiers*
Crete: *(Athens, Greece)*
Cyprus: *Nicosia*
Egypt: *Cairo*
Iran: *Tehran*
Iraq: *Baghdad*
Israel: *Jerusalem*
Jordan: *Amman*
Kuwait: *Kuwait City*
Lebanon: *Beirut*
Libya: *Tripoli*
Morocco: *Rabat*
Oman: *Muscat*
Qatar: *Doha*
Saudi Arabia: *Riyadh*
Syria: *Damascus*
Tunisia: *Tunis*
Turkey: *Ankara*
United Arab Emirates: *Abu Dhabi*
Yemen: *San'a*